The Technical Institute

The Technical Institute

MAURICE R. GRANEY

Dean, School of Engineering
University of Dayton

The Center for Applied Research in Education, Inc.
New York

Foreword

Prior to World War II, very few people in this country had heard of a technical institute, and those who were familiar with the term usually had no clear idea of what a technical institute was. Today there is a great deal of conversation about technical institutes, but profitable discussion is often hampered by the fact that the term means different things to different people. Even among educators, scientists, and engineers, there are no generally accepted definitions of terms such as technical institute or community college, of technical education as compared to vocational education, of post-high school education as opposed to college-level associate-degree education. The result is that when committees are formed to discuss such topics, a great deal of time has to be spent in finding a common language. There is no doubt that much of the disagreement that currently exists in the whole area of education beyond the high school is simply a reflection of the need for a careful definition of terms.

More important than definition is the need for a clearer understanding of the place of the technician in our complex organization of industry, business, the professions, and public service. As technology grows and permeates the lives of all of us, we find a growing demand for people who understand the facts, laws, systems, and machines on which our civilization is based. If we could provide a scientist properly trained to deal with every technical problem that has to be solved, we would have nothing to worry about. But of course this isn't possible. In fact, it is generally recognized that there is a shortage of scientists and engineers. There are simply not enough people available who have the necessary intelligence and interest and who are willing to pay the price of getting a solid education in science. So more and more scientists and engineers have to depend upon assistance from semiprofessional workers and technicians, conserving their own time for the problems that demand the highest

v

level of education and skill. Fortunately, there is a large pool of young people with an interest in science and engineering who are well-qualified for technician training and well-suited to make up the teams which are essential to the optimum use of our top-level talent.

This book by Maurice Graney describes what a technical institute is and how it goes about producing technicians to fill this great need in American society.

ERIC A. WALKER

President
The Pennsylvania State University

The Technical Institute

Maurice Graney

Maurice Graney's book *The Technical Institute* treats comprehensively all the many issues that have arisen and are still being debated about this relatively new and somewhat atypical unit in American higher education. The author points out the many needs for technicians in the modern productive economy, and the continuing shortages in technicians prepared. He comments on the relatively inferior status of the technician, as compared with a professional worker, in industry and in popular regard. The confusion that has surrounded the meaning of the term "technical institute" is explored and explained.

The author devotes much attention to the problems of curriculum building in the technical institute. Particular importance is attached to the two-year time limit, into which must be compressed not only the necessary theoretical knowledge and technical skills, but also some elements of general education. The contrast is sharply drawn between two schools of thought, one of which at the extreme would eliminate all except the purely technical subjects from the curriculum, the other of which would view the technician as a future citizen with a great need for an adequate background of general education.

The institutional organization for providing preparation for technicians is described under four general categories: private technical institutes, technical institute divisions of complex university systems, the publicly controlled local school, and other miscellaneous provisions. The emergence of the community college as an important agency for educating technicians is emphasized. On controversial issues, all points of view are given fair treatment, although Dean Graney does not hesitate to express his own opinions about suitable lines for future development.

Dean Graney's book is one of several in the Library of Education that deals with various kinds of institutions of higher education in the United States. It is parallel to such books already published in the series as: Carlson, *The Municipal University;* Wahlquist and Thornton, *State Colleges and Universities;* Mayhew, *The Smaller Liberal Arts College;* and Wicke, *The Church-Related College.*

JOHN DALE RUSSELL

Content Editor

Contents

CHAPTER I

Introduction

Definition of "Technical Institute"

In the United States, the term "technical institute" has a variety of meanings. Each of these meanings is evolving as society evolves. As refinements of thought emerge and as alternatives in both educational and social activities occur, the connotations of the term change. Outside the United States, the educational counterpart of the technical institute undergoes a simultaneous change, so that a complex of definitions arises. Each of these has some validity when used in its appropriate context and at the appropriate place and time. From this milieu two dominant concepts of the term emerge. One recognizes the technical institute as a type of education, the other as an educational institution. Frequently these conceptions are so intermixed in the thought of both laymen and professional educators that communication is difficult.

A type of education. As a type of education the technical institute can be compared to such educational fields as engineering, law, or nursing. Like them, it comprises study and its direct application to life. Viewed in this light, the technical institute is seen as a program of study, not as an institution *per se*. Certainly a polytechnical institute to educate engineers, a college of law to educate lawyers, and a nursing school to educate nurses are each a part of our society's educational complex; but so also are many multipurpose institutions which have specific programs of study designed to educate nurses, engineers, or lawyers as well as persons in other academic and professional disciplines. The fact that the institution has a single or a multiple purpose is irrelevant. The type of program itself, together with the graduate of this program, is central to the meaning attached to the terminology. When the technical institute is identified as a program of study, the person pursuing this program follows an orderly sequence of subject matter in his schooling, becomes prepared for productive and gainful employment, and may

1

work for an employer or engage in private practice. The program of study may be offered by an institution which has this as its only purpose, or it may be one of many programs offered by a comprehensive university.

Perhaps one reason why the meaning of technical institute is difficult to grasp is that the word "institute" normally denotes an institution. This is not true of such words as engineering, law, or nursing. Nor, for that matter, is it true of medicine, architecture, auto mechanics, electronics, business, or a host of other fields of study. Semantics influence thought. The terms "law school," "engineering school," and "nursing school" are a part of daily usage; but the term "technical institute school" is seldom, if ever, used. Yet when the term "technical institute" is conceived as denoting a program of study, "technical institute school" is consistent and correct.

The use of the term "technical institute" as a type of education has gained substantial acceptance in many educational circles. The phrase *curricula of technical institute type* is used in literature published by the Engineers' Council for Professional Development in connection with its accreditation activities. Such usage also is employed in the writings of persons in the United States Office of Education. In addition, this conception of the term is used in legal practice from time to time. Still another area of such usage is in the literature of some large universities. The University of Houston has a College of Technology offering technical institute curriculums. Similarly, technical institute programs are offered by the University of Toledo through its Community and Technical College and by the Oklahoma State University through its College of Engineering. Thus, the idea of the technical institute as a type of education is an important aspect of any definition of the term.

As an educational institution. Many prominent contributors to the literature on the technical institute conceive the term to mean an educational institution. In their comprehensive publication, *A Study of Technical Institutes,* Wickenden and Spahr identify the characteristics of a technical institute.[1] Smith and Lipsett define a technical institute as a *postsecondary institution.*[2] In fact, it is assumed by

[1] William E. Wickenden and Robert H. Spahr, *A Study of Technical Institutes* (Lancaster, Pennsylvania: Society for the Promotion of Engineering Education, 1931), now American Society for Engineering Education.

[2] Leo F. Smith and Laurence Lipsett, *The Technical Institute* (New York: McGraw-Hill Book Company, 1956), p. 3.

most writers in the field that the technical institute is an institution even though they may digress from this position at times.

When the term is interpreted as an institution, technical institutes can be identified with many kinds of organizational or administrative structures. Some technical institutes are single-purpose schools operated exclusively for the purpose of educating technicians. These schools may be privately or publicly supported. The privately supported may be proprietary or nonprofit, hold religious affiliation, be supported by industry, operated by a single individual, or administered by any of a wide variety of independent boards or corporations. Those which are publicly supported may derive support from municipal, county, state, or federal funds. In addition to single-purpose institutions are many multiple-purpose schools having technical institutes. A number of large universities support and operate a technical institute. Some municipal universities incorporate a technical institute into their structure. Schools operated by the armed forces occasionally have a technical institute in addition to other colleges or divisions.

There are also independent schools which are multipurpose in character but which restrict their offerings to kindred programs in a particular discipline. Such programs may include some at the vocational level and others at the college level. A junior college may have a technical institute and at the same time a division which offers university-parallel curriculums for students seeking transfer credit. Community colleges frequently include a technical institute in their structure. In his book, *The Technical Institute in America,* Henninger states that he directed questionnaires to 256 institutions, each of which presumably operated a technical institute.[3] This list included schools of the most divergent organization and structure.

Not all schools which qualify as technical institutes use the term in their school names and not all technical institute divisions of multipurpose institutions are identified by this term. Such terms as academy, school, college, community college, junior college, institute, polytechnic institute, and so on are used as names by single-purpose technical institutes. In the large comprehensive universities such division titles as college of technology, special courses division, division of technical studies, and similar names are used. Conversely,

---

[3] G. Ross Henninger, *The Technical Institute in America* (New York: McGraw-Hill Book Company, 1959), p. 185.

many institutions which do use the name technical institute, either
to define the institution or some division of it, do not meet the
definition by the statements of their purposes, by their operational
activities, or by both. Certainly, one cannot deny an institution the
permission to use the words "technical institute," but the mere ap-
pending of the title does not create the entity.

Some definitive characteristics. What then does the term "technical institute" mean? Perhaps it would be correct to define it as a
particular type of education, and to add that any institution or division of an institution offering this type of education is a technical
institute. This would be in agreement with the definition in the *Dictionary of Education* which defines the term as

an institution or division of an institution of higher learning offering instruction in one or more branches of technology frequently leading to an
associate degree; also applied to a tertiary type of education between that
of the skilled craftsman and the professional engineer.[4]

The type of education which rightly could be called technical institute has certain definite characteristics. These characteristics have
evolved over the years and constantly are undergoing subtle modifications. While there would be some bickering regarding fine points
of definition, regardless of what a technical institute program was
said to be, there is fairly uniform agreement upon the following
points.

1. *It is post-secondary.* This statement simply means that education of the technical institute type presupposes a student body composed of high school graduates or of individuals who have by some
device achieved equivalent educational status. The question of
whether or not such education is of college grade level is unanswered
by this statement. In fact, there is some disagreement about the
meaning of "college grade." The U.S. Office of Education saw fit
in 1946 to publish a bulletin entitled *Vocational Education of College Grade* in which this meaning is discussed.[5] This discussion
points out that the word *college* may mean an institution, or it may
mean a level in the scheme of educational organization—elementary
school, high school, and college. The bulletin goes on to state:

---

[4] Carter V. Good, ed., *Dictionary of Education* (New York: McGraw-Hill
Book Company, 1959), p. 554.
[5] *Vocational Education of College Grade,* Bulletin 1946, No. 18 (Washington,
D.C.: U.S. Office of Education, 1946), p. 4.

It must be understood that the term "college" is used in the latter sense in this report. College is a level in the vertically organized educational system of this country. As a system evolves, as the high schools change, as the types of students entering the college level change, the character of the college changes. It must serve the educational needs of all who wish, and qualify for, education beyond the high school level. It must have curricula of various lengths and leading to all sorts of occupational ends. It includes technical institutes, business colleges, junior colleges, normal schools, thirteenth and fourteenth grade schools, extension centers, and the like, as well as the better understood 4-year colleges, teachers colleges, and universities. It is to this level of education that the report refers when it uses the expression "of college grade."

The term "college grade" was used in Title VIII of the National Defense Education Act in defining which programs were ineligible to receive federal funds supporting education of the type defined.[6] In this connection, the point has been made by some educators that grade and level suggest different interpretations. For example, college grade might mean schooling leading to the baccalaureate degree, whereas college level might mean any schooling beyond the high school, or vice versa. In any event, even though there may be debate about the meaning of college grade or level, there is fairly uniform understanding of the term "post-secondary." Technical institute education is post-secondary.

2. *It is essentially terminal.* Here again one encounters some confusion in the understanding of a word that is used repeatedly in educational circles. The use of the phrase *terminal program of study* suggests that once the program is completed no further study can be pursued. This, of course, is not what is meant in regard to technical institute curriculums any more than it is meant in regard to curriculums in any professional field. No educational program can be genuinely terminal. What is meant here is that the program aims to encompass in its instruction the required material, both knowledges and skills, that a graduate needs to take his place as a productive practitioner in his field. Obviously, technical institute graduates can go forward with more study for the remainder of their lives if they so choose. But the program of study is such that, having completed it, a graduate is presumed to be qualified for employment.

3. *It is related to the fields of science and technology.* All tech-

6 Public Law 85–864, 85th Congress, H.R. 13247 (September 2, 1958).

nical institute education is essentially oriented to fields of applied science. Broadly speaking, it educates technicians who can work in support of professionals in these fields. Much emphasis is placed upon the education of engineering technicians in technical institute curriculums and it is true that the majority of students follow such programs. It would be inaccurate to suggest, however, that this is the only area which can be served by the technical institute. Laboratory technicians in the medical sciences, technicians supporting physicists or chemists in research, those assisting architects, and those who fill supporting supervisory positions in production industries are all technicians who validly could be educated in a technical institute.

4. *It offers intensive instruction in a brief period.* Most technical institute curriculums are for two academic years. A few are one year, and a few are three years. Such curriculums do not purport to cover the same scope of subject matter as the four-year baccalaureate programs. In general, the content is restricted and the coverage is intense, at times penetrating to unusual depth in a narrow field. Many times the subject matter covered is tailored to the precise needs of the employment situation. Technical institute courses are not designed to satisfy the requirements of similar courses in a baccalaureate program. Consequently, in most programs little of the credit earned can be transferred to a four-year bachelor program.

A number of institutions grant an associate degree for satisfactory completion of a technical institute program. Such a degree does not imply that the work completed is equivalent to the first two years of a four-year curriculum. The technical institute graduate in electrical technology, for example, would not have studied the same content as a student who completed the first two years of an electrical engineering program.

5. *It lays heavy emphasis upon application.* The typical technical institute program contains some theory, but generally only that which is essential for understanding the application. Laboratory content is heavy and considerable emphasis is placed upon manipulative activities. The intent is not to train the graduate as a skilled craftsman, but to make him conversant with the craftsman's work and problems. In a real sense, the technical institute graduate bridges the gap between the artisan and the professional. His schooling in-

cludes more theory than the craftsman needs and more craftsmanship than is usually possessed by the professional.

Perhaps there are other characteristics common to all technical
institute programs but the foregoing five compose an inescapable
minimum.

In the broad spectrum of educational enterprise, the technical
institute occupies that area between the high school and the professional school. It would be incorrect to assume, however, that this
area is so limited that all technical institute curriculums are identical
with regard to level, content, and direction. There is room for levels
within the technical institute area itself, and with the explosive
growth of science and technology this area inevitably will continue
to expand.

Historical Background

Other volumes of the Library of Education series cover the historical development of higher education. There are certain specifics
in this history, however, which bear precisely upon the technical institute and which should be brought into focus to insure an understanding of its place in the total educational structure.

The impact of national crises. Educational programs in general reflect the philosophies, the culture, and the needs of a people
at a given time and place. This is particularly true of technical education—when this term is used in its broadest sense. It has been
pointed out by Graney that technical education frequently lags be-
hind the development of a people and catches up, so to speak, in
spurts and starts, when crisis situations confront society.[7]

In colonial days and in the United States in its early years, there
was little need for formal technical education. Farmers and craftsmen learned their skills by apprenticeship and scientists were educated abroad. Influences upon the economy in the years leading up
to the Civil War altered the needs of the country so much that these
traditional sources of technical manpower were inadequate for a
peace-time economy and critically deficient for war. The war itself
crystallized thought and action concerning this technical manpower.
The result was federal legislation in the form of the Morrill Act,

[7] Maurice R. Graney, "The Function and Operation of Technical Institutes,"
Journal of Engineering Education (March 1949), p. 373.

which established the land grant colleges of engineering and agriculture.

A somewhat parallel situation existed in the economy in the years just before World War I. A large percentage of the supply of highly skilled craftsmen in the country was trained in Europe. The United States was dependent upon such immigrants to man its huge industrial plant and again was uncertain of itself in time of peace and vulnerable in time of war. As before, the impact of the war stimulated federal action and the resulting Smith-Hughes Vocational Education Act was aimed directly at correcting the deficiency in the supply of artisans.

In the interim period between World Wars I and II, the complexity of technology increased to such an extent that an incredible gap developed between the craftsmen and the professional engineers and scientists. The need for technicians to bridge this gap became paramount if the country was to gear its productive capacity up to the survival level.

Events leading up to World War II and the conflict itself compelled the government to establish the Engineering Defense Training Program and subsequently the Engineering, Science, Management War Training Program. Literally hundreds of thousands of technician-level specialists were trained during this period, resulting in an acute awareness on the part of educators that a genuine long-range technical institute program was an absolute must. It is true that not all forward motion in technical education is the result of crisis situations, but certainly they play a dynamic role.

Early beginnings. If it is accurate to say that the technical institute as it is known today reflects the need for well-educated technicians in a complex technology, it is only just to acknowledge that its history can be traced back for over two hundred years. Smith and Lipsett state that:

> The social and economic forces which gave rise to the technical institute began to find expression in the academy founded in 1751 by Franklin, who sought the improvement of agriculture, industry, and commerce through the application of science and reason.[8]

Wickenden and Spahr identify the Lyceum established at Gardiner, Maine, in 1822 as the first technical institute in the United States.[9]

---

[8] Smith and Lipsett, *The Technical Institute,* p. 18.
[9] Wickenden and Spahr, *A Study of Technical Institutes,* p. 31.

Others, such as the Ohio Mechanics Institute in Cincinnati, survive today.

Most of the early institutions which could be identified, even loosely, as technical institutes have long since passed from the picture. In part, they derived from the German *technikum* with its well-ordered technological curriculum at a definitely less than university level. In part, they derived from earlier "schools" which held lecture series to upgrade the populace in the developing mechanic arts. It is true that none of these were technical institutes by post-World War II definition, yet they were forerunners in a real sense. They were not colleges granting the baccalaureate degree. They were not secondary schools or academies offering preparatory work for college entrance. They geared their instruction to the maturing technology of the time, laying emphasis upon application with intensive instruction during short periods of less than four years. If they tended to prepare artisans, at least to some degree, it was because such artisans as they prepared were qualified, themselves, to bridge the gap between practice and theory. There were dozens of such institutions started during the nineteenth and early twentieth centuries. Most flourished for a period of time and then disappeared from the scene.

Some early technical institutes.   A few continued to operate and are among the educational institutions of the present. Some of these would be classified as technical institutes today. In addition to the Ohio Mechanics Institute (operating as the Ohio College of Applied Science since 1960), the Spring Garden Institute (1851), the Milwaukee School of Engineering (1903), the Franklin Technical Institute—now called The Franklin Institute of Boston (1908)—and Wentworth Institute (1911) are such schools. There are a few others. A large number of those which have continued to the present abandoned the objective for which they were founded and initiated four-year bachelor degree curriculums in fields of engineering and science. Among such schools are Pratt Institute, Drexel Institute, Brooklyn Polytechnic Institute, Carnegie Institute of Technology, and Bradley University. A fairly recent addition to this list is the Rochester Institute of Technology, which started in 1829 as the Rochester Athenaeum and Mechanics Institute and exerted genuine leadership in the technical institute field for many years.

The Wickenden-Spahr report. The institutions which started as technical institutes and which maintained this identity down through the years are few in number. Yet the need for a type of education lying between the secondary or the vocational school on the one hand and the professional school on the other has persisted and, in fact, has increased. It was this fact more than any other— the instability of the technical institute as a segment of American education—which prompted the Society for the Promotion of Engineering Education to include a study of technical institutes in its examination of engineering education in the late 1920's. (The Society is now the American Society for Engineering Education.)

This study was a collateral project of the 1923–29 investigation of engineering education; it was published in 1931. Credit for its authorship is generally attributed to William E. Wickenden and Robert H. Spahr, although many prominent educators participated in the study. The product of an engineering society, it has a definite engineering orientation. There were at the time, and are today, many educators who view this fact with some alarm, because they believe that the technical institute concept transcends the engineering limitation and that the subsequent implementation of this type of education thus has been limited. This study, however, profoundly affected educational thought and history. Since its publication, the engineering profession has exerted by far the most telling influence on the direction taken by technical institute education.

The Wickenden-Spahr study made certain penetrating observations and a number of recommendations. It noted that the American economy was understaffed in the scientific and technical field and estimated that the potential demand for engineering college graduates was only one-third supplied. More critically, the desirable quota of employees having approximately two years of post-secondary technical training was not more than one-fiftieth supplied. It pointed out further that although private enterprise had supported important technical institutes, the actual needs were beyond the resources of such agencies. It was estimated some 250 institutes were needed. This seemed to call for the creation of a great chain of institutions having an organic place in tax-supported systems. The report held that a distinctive type of institution was needed if it were to achieve permanency and success. It held out little hope for the success of auxiliary departments of standard engineering colleges because such technical education could become a salvage for failures in the longer courses and lose a positive appeal of its own. It also took a dim view of the junior college as an agency to do the work of a technical institute because in fulfilling its purposes the junior college would tend to mold all curriculums into the truncated college course pattern. The report states that:

> Whenever its distinctive aims are not clearly visualized and tenaciously pursued, the technical institute tends to drift into the college field, often to the neglect of the very groups it was created to serve.[10]

This report took the position that technical institute education should be geared to the technology of particular industries rather than to the broad aims of generalized engineering courses. It underscored the validity of identifying curriculums with the needs of particular geographical regions. In addition, it recognized the crucial role of the independent proprietary institution in trail-blazing educational areas not otherwise provided for, but it foresaw the precarious nature of education which pays its own way and faces the temptation to engage in "window dressing."

One of the most acute observations in the report deals with the lack of solidarity among the then existing technical institutes. Each institution, having grown up around some person or some local situation, sought to preserve its own individuality. This caused emphasis to be placed upon dissimilarities and mitigated against such things as a uniform credential for graduates, a sense of professional integration, an organization, and a forum for airing common problems. What was badly needed, the report stated, was some means of closer association. Some central body of high standing should be concerned with technical institute education as a whole. Though the authors were committed unequivocally to the position that technical institutes develop engineering technicians, they felt that if the engineering profession were to assume this responsibility, the result might be to bias the development of technical institute courses. They concluded by stating that this "matter must remain inconclusive until the representatives of the technical institutes are themselves prepared to take the initiative."[11]

Because the publication of this report coincided with the great

---

[10] *Ibid.*, p. 9.
[11] *Ibid.*, p. 15.

depression of the thirties, few schools were financially able to implement the recommendations made. When the depression eased and when World War II became imminent, technical institute curriculums emerged at many institutions. In the forefront of the resurgence was the engineering profession. Some of the country's most prominent universities with distinguished engineering colleges initiated technical institute programs. The Pennsylvania State University, Purdue University, the Georgia Institute of Technology, and the Oklahoma State University were among these. The American Society for Engineering Education began to devote increasing attention to the topic in its meetings and publications. The Engineers' Council for Professional Development, which had for some years served as the official accrediting agency for engineering curriculums, established a subcommittee for the accreditation of technical institute curriculums. The contribution to the literature in the field by engineering educators and professional engineers increased markedly. In fact, the pervasive voice of engineering was so articulate that the term "technical institute" became identified once and apparently for all as a part of engineering.

Other influences. This does not mean that the field was exclusively pre-empted by engineering. There were other groups which, as time passed, participated in the development of this type of education. In all but a few instances, however, the resulting actions were either oriented toward engineering or were on the periphery of engineering activity. New York State, for example, established a number of agricultural and technical colleges in several communities. Most of these offer, as a central part of the program, curriculums of the technical institute type designed to develop engineering technicians. California concerned itself with the establishment of engineering-oriented technical institute curriculums in its community and junior colleges. Florida and Texas also have moved in this direction. Certain of the nation's larger industries have recognized technical institute education as a source of supply for personnel who become a part of the engineering team.

The junior college influence. As pointed out above, there was some activity regarding this type of education which was taken by groups that were not engineering-oriented. These have asserted a significantly different educational philosophy, which has influenced technical institute education. One of these is the group identified with the junior college-community college movement. While it is recognized that there are differences existing in this broad educational grouping, there is nonetheless a consistent philosophical approach which permeates the thought of its exponents.

This approach holds pre-eminent the requirement that all formal education retain as its central theme the education of the whole individual—spiritually, physically, vocationally. Whether the goal be to prepare a person through university parallel courses for advanced work toward the baccalaureate or to prepare him through a terminal program for entry-level employment, the central theme is unchanged. In part, the attempt to achieve this goal is made through the general education component in the program of study. Sometimes this is simply a series of courses in English, history, government, and so on. At other times, a more integrated approach is used wherein a careful correlation of various disciplines blends a unifying general education influence throughout a program of study. In any case, the education of the whole individual takes precedence over the development of a particular isolated competency. This philosophical approach differs markedly from that held by most proponents of technical institute education of the traditional type in which the central theme is technical competence. In most instances this technical competence is quite narrow.

The influence of the junior college-community college group upon the technical institute type of education has been exerted through terminal education programs. These have been designed to prepare technicians for semiprofessional employment in business, industry, and government. While the number and percentage of such programs has increased steadily in the published offerings of such schools, the actual enrollments in these programs have been quite limited. This has been verified by Bogue, who traced the study of several investigators during the period from 1917 through 1948. He found that catalog listings of technical programs rose from 18 per cent to 47 per cent in that period, but he goes on to state:

> When we make a closer examination of the curricular enrollments, however, it is found that a relatively small percentage of students are actually in technical programs. . . .
> Moreover, presence of veterans in the colleges did not appear to have changed enrollments on the percentage basis for agriculture or for industrial or trade occupations. It is true that the numbers in

1947–48 were almost twice as great as they were ten years previous, but the percentages remained almost the same in spite of all that was said about the veteran student wanting short-cut education of a more practical nature for immediate and usable skill occupations. If Hillmer had included privately controlled institutions in his investigation, it is quite likely that an even higher percentage of students would have been found in general cultural curricula, because many of these institutions are for women. The prevailing type in respect to enrollment in public junior colleges is coeducational. As possible interpretations of Hillmer's findings, it appears that either there were more students on the whole who wanted general cultural education, or that those who wanted short-cut occupational training did not enroll in junior colleges.[12]

The role of the junior or community college of the future, however, may be a dominant one. Some rapprochement of the two differing philosophies could trigger an expansion of junior college enrollments in terminal curriculums of the technical institute type to such an extent that such schools would be the main suppliers of technician personnel in all employment categories. It is worthy of note, however, that the influence to date reflects a philosophy which contrasts with that exerted by the traditional technical institute.

The vocational educational influence. A second group espousing a philosophy which differs from that of the engineering-oriented educators is the vocational education segment of the secondary schools. Historically, this group concerned itself with the training of skilled craftsmen and the education of their teachers. Students were prepared for jobs requiring high degrees of skill in the use of their hands and of trade judgment in industry. As industry progressed and the need for technicians of definite technical competency began to displace the need for skilled mechanics, the vocational educators established vocational-technical programs of less than college grade. Inevitably, this movement toward technician education brought them into contact with the engineering educators moving into the field of technician education from a different direction. Unfortunately, the educational terminology employed by both groups was the same but definitions and basic philosophies were different.

In 1944 the United States Commissioner of Education, John W.

<hr>

[12] Jesse Parker Bogue, *The Community College* (New York: McGraw-Hill Book Company, 1950), p. 191.

Studebaker, in his foreword to *Vocational-Technical Training for Industrial Occupations* stated:

> There was a time when the term "less than college grade" was relatively easily defined, especially in terms of responsibility for determining standards and for administration. But in recent years with the expansion of all forms of occupational education operating under such terms as vocational education, vocational-technical training, technical education, a considerable amount of confusion has·developed with respect to the differences among these types and levels of training.[13]

Since the time of Dr. Studebaker's statement, both groups have continued to use the same words and to give them different connotations. The difference is reflected in programs of study, the objectives of such programs, and in the end product of the educational endeavor. A technician graduated from a technical institute program administered by vocational education personnel is job-oriented. He has been trained in a program aimed at the needs of a closely-knit family of occupations. Courses in the program, for example, are designed to qualify the graduate for entry employment in a job. Likewise, teachers in the program are selected because of their knowledge of the job activity and their ability to impart this knowledge. The technician is given training with an occupational objective.

In contrast with this, the technician graduated from an engineering-oriented technical institute is educated to work in a supporting role to a professional. Greater emphasis is placed upon a subject-matter area or an academic discipline than upon job preparation. He is taught by individuals who intend to imbue him with an approach to a problem, or a method of attack, so that he can assist the professional at work rather than perform in a job. Generally speaking, the mathematical and science component of his program of study is more rigorous, more classical, more likely to be taught as discreet subject matter. As he pursues the curriculum, he develops a close kinship to a profession rather than to an occupation. Much of the subject matter for both types of technician may appear to be similar, but there is a crucial difference in the total educational experience. It is irrelevant at this juncture to attempt to determine

[13] *Vocational-Technical Training for Industrial Occupations*, Vocational Division Bulletin No. 228 (Washington, D.C.: U.S. Office of Education, 1944), p. vii.

which approach is better, which worse, or to assess which comes closer to meeting the real needs of the industrial economy. It is important to recognize that here are two philosophies quite separate, yet using identical terminology.

The impact of the vocational educators upon technical institute education is unquestionably significant. The National Defense Education Act of 1958 gave considerable momentum to their influence through the provisions enunciated in Title VIII:

> It is therefore the purpose of this title to provide assistance to the States so that they may improve their vocational education programs through area vocational education programs approved by the State boards of vocational education. . . .[14]

This Title includes an amendment to the Vocational Education Act of 1946 and in Section 307(d) states:

> The term "area vocational education program" means a program consisting of one or more less-than-college-grade courses conducted under public supervision and control on an organized, systematic class basis, which is designed to fit individuals for useful employment as technicians or skilled workers in recognized occupations requiring scientific or technical knowledge, and which is made available to residents of the State or an area thereof designated and approved by the State board, who either have completed junior high school, or regardless of their school credits, are at least sixteen years of age and can reasonably be expected to profit by the instruction offered.[15]

Summary.   In summary it may be stated that in the United States technical institute education has deep roots in the unique, limited-purpose schools established from time to time throughout the country. These schools have been embraced, developed, and refined by engineering educators. The junior college-community college influence has been felt to some degree, as has the influence of the vocational education program in the public school systems. On the whole, however, the technical institute has developed as an engineering-oriented segment of the total educational structure.

---

[14] Public Law 85–864, 85th Congress, H.R. 13247 (September 2, 1958).
[15] *Ibid.,* amendment 1946, Section 397(d).

Technician Education Outside the United States

In many of its aspects the education of technicians in other industrial countries has paralleled that of the United States, both in its historical growth and in the comprehensiveness of its coverage. This has occurred because the advances in science have been freely disseminated on a world-wide basis and the impact of the industrial revolution has touched all of the more advanced western societies. In England and continental Europe population pressures long ago triggered intense economic competition both within and between national populations, making some centralized direction of education practically a requirement for national survival. In this milieu, technical education has been conceived as a national problem. Its organization, direction, and control have been carefully planned. The resulting system selects its students in a way that reflects not only social cleavages but also acceptance of the fact that education is an exacting intellectual process and not a sentimental privilege. Early advances in technical education in the mature European economies proceeded at a more rapid pace than in the United States. On the whole, however, the development of technical education from the early 1800's to the present has been quite similar in the United States and in other industrial countries.

Elsewhere in the world the education of technicians has been embraced more recently or is still unrecognized as a formal educational endeavor. Rapid catch-up strides have been made in Canada, Australia, Japan, and Russia in recent years. Some Latin American countries, India, Pakistan, and selected countries in the Near East and Africa are on the threshold of real development. There are, however, many places in the world with hundreds of millions in population where technician education, or all technical education at any level for that matter, is practically nonexistent.

England and Europe. The feature which most distinguishes technician education in the United States from technician education in Europe lies not in its content, but in its administration and purpose. Education in general in the United States may reflect national policy and be geared to the economic system, but its control or standardization is self-imposed. This has not been the case in Europe, as was pointed out by Wickenden and Spahr:

The several European systems, while not wholly free from accidental features, represent careful planning, based on a clearly perceived social philosophy. Their schools are much less individual enterprises than our own.[16]

The people of the United States have had little desire to reproduce the central-government direction and control of European states. With the passage of time both systems are tending to converge toward a middle ground between control and freedom. Perhaps the mounting economic and population pressures in the United States make tighter controls the inevitable result of a maturing society. Perhaps, also, European educators have viewed American industrial advance as an ultimate product of a free educational activity. In any case, certain modifications are creeping into each system.

In his comprehensive volume *Britain's Scientific and Technological Manpower,* Payne devotes a chapter to nonuniversity channels to a technical education.[17] He carefully traces the national concern about technical education as it relates to Great Britain's industrial position and its capacity to meet the threat of foreign competition.

Technical education beyond the secondary level is carried on through the so-called establishments for further education which embrace technical colleges and other nonuniversity institutions. Such establishments, along with educational programs of local industries, lean heavily upon evening classes for persons who are fully employed and offer an almost limitless number of areas of specialization. A typical fifteen-year-old may study seven, eight, or nine years part-time, sit for his examination, and be certified as a technician. The Ministry of Education and the professional society concerned work jointly on examinations and certification. The heavy emphasis upon part-time study is not regarded as a fault, but as a virtue, and the success of the "earning while learning" program supports this position.

Canada.   There is some carry-over from the British system in the certification of technical personnel in Canada. The technical institute type of education is spreading throughout Canada, is organized separately in the several provinces, and perhaps has reached the highest level in Ontario. In this province there are six Institutes

---

16 Wickenden and Spahr, *A Study of Technical Institutes,* p. 199.
17 George Louis Payne, *Britain's Scientific and Technological Manpower* (Stanford, California: Stanford University Press, 1960).

of Technology offering programs requiring up to three years of full-time study to persons who have completed the secondary school. The Association of Professional Engineers of the Province of Ontario grants certification in four grades: three as engineering technicians and one, the highest, as engineering technologist. All certifications require specified minimums of formal education and practical experience. Other provinces are developing similar programs. Quebec, which has a somewhat different educational system, has a number of institutions giving programs of this type.

Russia. The post-World War II upsurge in Russian productivity and the spectacular achievements in space focused the attention of many American educators upon the Russian system of technical education. In 1958, the American Society for Engineering Education sent an engineering education exchange mission to the Soviet Union. In 1960, the Engineers Joint Council dispatched a delegation to the U.S.S.R. to study the training, placement, and utilization of engineers and technicians, and the following year the American Association of Junior Colleges sponsored a United States technical education delegation under the Cultural Exchange Agreement between the two countries. Each of these published its findings so that a rather comprehensive coverage of Russian activity in the field became available. In addition, Korol's *Soviet Education for Science and Technology* describes in detail the organization structure, purpose, and operation of the system.[18]

From these sources it becomes evident that the Russian system carries to its extreme the notion of centralized control that pervades to a lesser degree the European systems, and which is practically unthinkable in the United States. The A.S.E.E. team stated:

> In order to understand the engineering educational system in the U.S.S.R., some consideration must be given to the political and social framework within which this system operates. The whole economy of the U.S.S.R. is integrated into a broad plan devised by the state planning commission (GOSPLAN). The formulation of the position of the master plan related to engineering education is the responsibility of the Ministry of Higher Education. A long-range plan, covering a period normally of five years, is formulated first. Each year the master plan is modified to take into account the accomplishments of the previous year. The plan considers the needs

---

[18] Alexander G. Korol, *Soviet Education for Science and Technology* (New York: John Wiley & Sons, Inc., 1957).

of the whole Soviet Union in the light of the proposed expansion of industrial plant capacity and the need for personnel to provide for this expansion and for retirements, replacements, and up-grading. The master plan specifies the number who may enter the institutions of higher education, the number who may train for each field of specialization, the quota of each specific institution for each speciality and the jobs available at the time of graduation.[19]

The Soviet system is so organized that after ten years of elementary and middle school, a student may enter higher education at either the university or the technical institution, the latter for engineering education, or he may enter the *technicum,* which offers education of the technical institute type. The university or technical institution program lasts from five to six years and the technicum program about two and one-half years. Students also may enter the technicum after seven years of schooling, but then must study for four years rather than two and one-half years.

The report of the Engineers Joint Council delegation states that the group was permitted to visit three technicums. It further states:

> These brief contacts with Soviet technicum education hardly justify reaching definite conclusions regarding this system of education, embracing as it does some 3,500 secondary specialized schools, of which one-third are engineering related technicums. . . . Nevertheless, certain facts were obtained and impressions were gained which led us to some conclusions regarding technicum education in the Soviet union.
>
> The Soviets have established an extensive educational program to produce engineering technicians. From approximately 1,200 technicums of the 3,500 secondary specialized schools in the Soviet Union, they claim to be graduating 250,000 young people each year to enter specialized industrial employment. This represents a graduating class of approximately 200 per school. One-third of these graduates are women. These graduates complete either full-time day programs, part-time evening programs, or part-time correspondence programs. . . . In contrast with this, we graduate approximately 16,000 technicians per year in the United States, of whom not more than 1,000 are of the quality produced in the three technicums that we visited in the U.S.S.R.[20]

[19] American Society for Engineering Education, "Engineering Education Exchange Mission to the Soviet Union," *Journal of Engineering Education* (May 1959), p. 844.

[20] *The Training, Placement, and Utilization of Engineers and Technicians in the Soviet Union* (New York: Engineers Joint Council, 1961), p. 21.

The delegation sponsored by the American Association of Junior Colleges reported:

> The curriculum in the Soviet technicum is characterized by a high degree of narrow specialization. The program of study, historically and currently, is devoted largely to the development of a skill and a technical knowledge in a particular trade or technical specialty associated with a specific industry. A very important feature of the technicum curriculum is the requirement for actual on-the-job work experience.[21]

All who have had first-hand contact with the Russian program seem to be in agreement on certain fundamental points. The technicums are well-equipped, staffed, and administered. The faculties are fully qualified in their fields by both formal education and work experience, though some lack adequate personal qualifications and skill as teachers. The student body is carefully selected and qualified, and student motivation is high. Job opportunities and status recognition for graduates is such that any effort expended is rewarded. Since only a limited number of schools were visited by any group, all visiting teams suspect that there must be wide variations among the many technicums, and, no doubt, some are of poorer quality than those which were visited.

---

[21] *Report of the United States Technical Education Delegation to the Union of Soviet Socialist Republics* (Washington, D.C.: American Association of Junior Colleges, 1961), p. 23.

CHAPTER II

The Technical Institute
and Present-Day Technology

The Emerging Role of the Technician

Present-day industry is based upon a technology rooted in science. The history of the development of scientific information is common knowledge. The rate of this development has been accelerating exponentially, so that in recent decades the more advanced world societies have been almost overwhelmed with an information explosion. Men have attempted to harness this information with a technology which would convert it to useful purposes. Industries built around the continually developing technologies have utilized new materials and processes in an ever-widening spiral. Today the productivity resulting from such enterprise has brought an incredibly high standard of living, but this productivity is completely dependent upon a carefully educated and skillfully trained manpower.

The technical spectrum. Ever since the dawn of the industrial era, it has been observed that, first, the dependence of productivity upon unskilled labor has been diminishing, and, second, the communication gap between designer and worker has been widening. Both of these trends have accelerated at a rate comparable to the growth of industrial enterprise. These trends mean that increasing numbers of workers who in an earlier period would have served as unskilled laborers must acquire an ability to perform at a higher level. The trends also mean that the designer himself has moved upward in the realm of creativity so far that the aforementioned communication gap is vast enough to require a whole spectrum of technicians to bridge it. Automation has taken over much of the drudgery of industry, and scientists and engineers have concerned themselves more and more with complex equipment such as nuclear reactors and electronic computers.

It has become increasingly apparent that the need for technicians, the middle men of modern ingenious productivity, is crucial and, for the most part, unmet. As early as 1926, surveys revealed that more technicians were needed than four-year engineering graduates, in ratios ranging from 2.6 technicians to one engineer in some types of industry to much higher ratios in other types. At that time the over-all actual ratio was one technician to five engineers.[1] Since then, and particularly since World War II, dozens of agencies have made similar surveys or studies. Without exception they report a need for more technicians than engineers and an actual count of more engineers than technicians.

The National Science Foundation reported (NSF 61–75, "Scientific and Technical Personnel in Industry—1960") a survey covering an estimated 95 per cent of the total number employed in industrial firms and in their own businesses in 1960. This survey showed 648,900 engineers and 594,000 technicians. At that same time, surveys concerning the utilization of professional and technician personnel generally concluded that for maximum utilization of engineering and scientific manpower four to five technicians for each professional were needed. Congressman John Brademus, in discussing the proposed Technical Education Act of 1962 (H.R. 10396), quoted a statement by Paul H. Robbins, Executive Director of the National Society of Professional Engineers:

> There is virtual unanimity of agreement among manpower specialists both in and out of government that the shortage is extensive. . . . Unless there is an immediate and significant expansion of technical institute programs, we may well be underutilizing our professional engineering manpower by anywhere from 50 to 75 per cent.[2]

In addition to increasing quantitative requirements for technicians in our society, the last few decades have seen an incredible multiplication of the qualitative requirements. The use of complex electronic gear, for example, takes over the tasks of many production workers, but at the same time requires the services of highly trained technicians. The over-all result is a reduction in total manpower

---

[1] William E. Wickenden and Robert H. Spahr, *A Study of Technical Institutes* (Lancaster, Pennsylvania: Society for the Promotion of Engineering Education, 1931), p. 48.
[2] John Brademus, "New Frontiers in Technical Education." An address at the meeting of the Amercian Society for Engineering Education, U.S. Air Force Academy, June 1962.

needed, a vastly increased productivity per worker, and a high level of education for almost all involved.

There is also a high order of fragmentation of one scientific idea into a myriad of technologies. A 1961 publication by the United States Department of Labor describes 65 general and specific activities which are composites of analyses of certain positions which support engineers and scientists in industry.[3] Some of the activities described are: design draftsman, ram-jet engine; computer laboratory technician; electronics technician, nuclear reactor; flutter and vibration technologist, aircraft; analytical research technician, resins and adhesives; and development reactor technician, test apparatus. It is probably correct to state that no one of these job activities existed prior to World War II, and all are representative of a great multiplicity of technologies resulting from scientific advances. The brochure also describes the nature of the work done as well as the various aptitudes required to do the work. Each category requires the application of mathematical procedures involving analytical geometry, calculus, or vector analysis, as well as the application of the principles of physics or chemistry. In addition, many specific jobs require motor coordination and manual dexterity. In sum, the qualitative requirements for many technicians embrace new knowledges at a relatively high level and in complex relationships.

Some future projections. What of the future? Every signpost points to an immediate future in which the characteristics of the present will be retained and perhaps intensified. Harold Goldstein, Chief, Division of Manpower and Employment Statistics, Bureau of Labor Statistics, pointed out in 1961:

> . . . the rate of increase for professional and technical workers is expected to be over 40 per cent in this decade, double the rate of growth of the whole labor force; I want to add that the rate of growth for engineering and technical workers may be as high as 80 per cent, or double the rate of growth for the professional and technical occupations as a whole. What does this imply for the technicians? We now have some 700,000 technicians of whom about half are engineering and physical science technicians, about one-third are draftsmen, and the remaining one-sixth biological, agricultural, and other technicians. If this group of 700,000 is to increase by about 80 per cent and if we are to replace those who die and

---

[3] United States Department of Labor, *Technical Occupations in Research, Design, and Development* (Washington, D.C.: USGPO, February 1961).

retire, we will need to have about 70,000 people a year entering the
the ranks of technicians.[4]

In the face of this projection, the Engineering Manpower Commission reported a survey by one of its members, Donald C. Metz,
which showed an academic 1961–62 enrollment of only 40,000
full-time students in technical institutes. This represented a drop of
9 per cent from the number enrolled in 1957. Metz further states:

> This means our already short supply of engineers will be further
> handicapped by an even shorter supply of capable engineering tech-
> nicians to help carry forward the nation's technological commit-
> ments. The inevitable result will be some extremely undesirable
> utilization practices. Engineering technician shortages will force
> assignment of highly technical functions to those who are poorly
> qualified. Even less desirable, many highly qualified engineers will
> waste precious time with work which could better be done by com-
> petent engineering technician associates.[5]

While the projection of the supply of technicians in the immediate future indicates a genuine shortage, there is some reason to
believe that the long-range projection, after 1970, might not be so
bleak. The fact of a critical deficiency itself stimulates concern and
eventual action. During the late 1950's and early 1960's, a number
of agencies evidenced such concern. One of these, the National Association of Manufacturers, in 1957 published a booklet, *Your Opportunities in Industry as a Technician.* Directed at high school
students and laying emphasis upon the increasing technical complexity of industry, the booklet stated:

> The more revolutionary the discovery the more urgent becomes
> the need for people with special skills and training—people who
> are able to help translate scientific ideas and discoveries into useful
> products and services. This is the assignment of the technician. And
> industry needs an average of between five and seven technicians for
> every *one* professional engineer.[6]

In addition, a number of States conducted need surveys to help
guide the development of technician education programs. In 1962

4 *The Emerging Role of the Engineering Technician* (Dayton, Ohio: Proceedings
of a Conference held under the auspices of the Executive Office of the President,
Office of Civil Defense Mobilization, June 1961), p. 5.

5 *Engineering and Scientific Manpower Newsletter* (New York: Engineers Joint
Council, April 1962), p. 1.

6 *Your Opportunities in Industry as a Technician* (New York: National Association of Manufacturers, 1957), p. 7.

the U.S. Office of Education published an annotated bibliography of *Surveys and Studies in Vocational-Technical Education*. In this publication, which dealt only with technical programs under public school direction, 79 surveys in 25 states plus the District of Columbia and Puerto Rico were reported. Somewhat earlier the President's Committee on Education Beyond the High School stimulated many states to set up commissions to study problems on a statewide basis. Typical of these was the Ohio Commission on Education Beyond the High School, which published a report that dealt, in part, with engineering and related education. This report stated:

> Assuming that resources can be obtained to provide for the unfilled need for scientists, engineers and scholars, many with advanced degrees, deans of the engineering schools, industrial and labor leaders all stress another requirement. This is for technical assistants in a ratio of five or six to each engineer. Because Ohio is limited to six such facilities at the present time, none of which is publicly supported, the most immediate need in terms of new facilities is for two-year technical institutes in which engineering technicians can be trained and others can be prepared for operational work in an age of automation.[7]

The Federal Government also stimulated a number of conferences designed to focus attention on the long-range actions which should be taken. These conferences were under the auspices of the Executive Office of the President through the Office of Emergency Planning. One such conference held in January, 1962, dealt with the *Role of Women in Engineering Technology*. In summarizing the conference, Dr. William G. Torpey, Consultant in the Office of Emergency Planning stated:

> Specific requirements by U.S.A. industry for engineering and technological personnel far exceed the number of people entering the profession during the past few years. If this trend continues, many people without engineering degrees inevitably will enter the profession to fill the gap. . . . Companies should publicize the fact that they will employ women in these capacities.[8]

---

[7] *Ohio's Future In Education Beyond the High School* (Privately printed Final Report of the Commission on Education Beyond the High School, December 1958), p. 55.

[8] *The Role of Women in Engineering Technology* (Miami, Florida: Proceedings of a conference held under the auspices of the Executive Office of the President, Office of Engineering Planning, January 1962), p. 40.

The concern evidenced by these selected examples was echoed across the country. The total impact of such attention cannot be measured fully until sufficient time elapses for resulting action to take place. It seemed inevitable to all involved, however, that eventually the deficiency would be remedied and that the role of the technician in the technology of the future would emerge to a dominance far beyond any possible forecast.

The Technician and Higher Education

The traditional structure. Education in the United States has been influenced by a number of deep-seated convictions. At least two of these reflect the idea that a democratic government must rest upon an educated electorate. Translated into the structure of an educational system, these convictions are (1) that each person must be provided the opportunity to go to school, and (2) that the door should always be open to the individual to progress in school as far as personal qualifications permit. Given the capacity and the motivation, no one should be shunted into a *cul de sac* because of his status in society or his inadvertent election of a particular program of study. The educational ladder starting at the lowest elementary level must be designed to carry one upward unerringly. In the United States the son of an unskilled laborer need not be an unskilled laborer himself; the birthright of the son of a scholar is no greater in the educational system than the birthright of the son of an illiterate immigrant.

Thus, the door to progression has been open for movement through elementary, secondary, and higher education. The credential from grade school has been the entry to high school; the high school diploma has been the ticket to college. If the specific high school program followed by a particular person stressed a vocational or commercial education, a college preparatory content—perhaps minimal—has been included. The junior college program has led to the university or institute of technology; the bachelor degree, to the master; the master, to the doctorate. Obviously, particular programs of higher education have not been integrated with all other programs; a law student, for example, could not transfer unimpeded to a medical program. The significant fact has remained, however, that each led eventually to the top.

There have been exceptions to the rule, but in general the pattern has been well-established. In the recent past, however, this historical position has been yielding slowly. So-called terminal curriculums have been creeping into the system. The terminal aspect has occurred when such emphasis has been placed upon achievement of a vocational objective that some fundamental content, which underlies more advanced study, has been slighted. If the student wishes to continue to more advanced levels, he must master new fundamentals in order to carry onward and upward in his field. The technical institute curriculums of the present are of the so-called terminal type.

Social acceptability. It is because of the terminal nature of technical institute curriculums that many forsee an almost insurmountable obstacle barring the way to full implementation of this type of education to meet the needs of the time. A society so habituated to education which permits achievement of occupational goals simultaneously with progression up the educational ladder finds it hard to settle for less. And in an economy as free-wheeling as that of the United States, it appears that the majority place greater value upon upward educational progression than upon achievement of vocational competence.

This attitude of society toward the status value of terminal education is a major obstacle retarding the growth of technical institutes and the production of the much-needed engineering technicians. It is possible that no amount of reasoning can overcome the inertia of such an attitude. This was lucidly stated by Professor Donald C. Metz in an article, "Role of Engineering Technicians in the Decade of the 1960's."

> . . . much is needed to be done in the realm of the engineering technician for his social and professional status. The Carnegie Foundation in commenting in the *Quarterly* regarding the need for technicians pointed out that one of the major obstacles to the development of technical institute education for engineering technicians is the cult of the BA degree. This has become such a status symbol that many people give no thought to the education one needs or is capable of acquiring but rather blindly charge ahead, often unsuccessfully, for a Bachelor's Degree.[9]

9 Donald C. Metz, "Role of Engineering Technicians in the Decade of the 1960's," Proceedings of the Conference on Technical Manpower Retraining and Utilization, *Akron Technical Topics,* Vol. 12, No. 4 (April 1962), p. 24.

Summary.   For many decades the swift pace of science has stimulated the development of new technologies. This in turn has created a need for more and more engineers, technicians, and highly skilled craftsmen. The need is not only increasing quantitatively but is shifting in the direction of greater technical competence. The result is a demand for new types of schools which place emphasis upon developing technical capability in individuals who can operate the vast and complicated industrial plant. Such schools do not easily fit into the pattern of higher education which is the American heritage. An acute awareness of the need signals a widespread development of these schools, yet the weight of tradition may keep intact the system which terminates in the bachelor degree: a symbol of status as well as of education.

CHAPTER III

The Organization and Administration
of Technical Institute Education

Technical institute curriculums are offered by many types of institutions. It was pointed out in Chapter I that these vary in organization structure and administration to such a degree that no common description fits all. The institutions may be grouped arbitrarily in a variety of ways and for convenience in this presentation are placed in four general categories. Each category has characteristics which define a kind of institution distinct in some ways from institutions in other categories. These four are (1) private technical institutes, (2) technical institute divisions of complex university systems, (3) publicly controlled local technical institutes, and (4) all others.

Private Technical Institutes

Private technical institutes may be classified as either nonprofit or proprietary schools. The nonprofit schools derive their income from tuition, gifts and grants, endowments, and other sources not based on taxes. The resources of such schools are markedly different. Many meet operating deficits only through gifts from industry or other private donors, but a few operate on rather substantial endowments plus tuition. The proprietary schools, however, most frequently derive operating funds as well as capital funds from tuition alone. Frequently, proprietary schools will offer some programs of study outside the technical institute field, and not uncommonly finance a major portion of technical institute resident programs through income derived from correspondence study.

In his survey of 1957, Henninger found that 144 of the schools surveyed offered bona fide technical institute curriculums and of this number 52 were privately supported.[1] His definition of a tech-

[1] G. Ross Henninger, *The Technical Institute in America* (New York: McGraw-Hill Book Company, 1959), p. 4.

nical institute curriculum, however, included only those at the upper end of the spectrum. If a less restrictive definition is employed, the number of private schools reaches a much higher figure, with most of the increase resulting from the inclusion of a host of proprietary schools. It is not known how many of these offer curriculums that could be classified as technical institute in type but at a lower spectrum level. It is certain to be above 52, perhaps over 200 with some marginal institutions included. This number would include programs which are a part of the educational activity of certain industries. Whether or not such operations could be called nonprofit or proprietary is a moot point.

Nonprofit institutions. Private nonprofit technical institutes are normally structured much like any other institution of higher education. Whether endowed or deriving funds from tuition plus gifts and grants, they have the typical three-part organization of business office, instruction, and student welfare. Some also engage in research. The faculty is organized departmentally with the departments having the customary responsibility and authority. Conditions of faculty service—academic freedom, tenure, class load, vacations, and so forth—are quite similar to those found in most colleges. In certain regions of the country, these technical institutes may seek institutional accreditation through the accrediting association of the region as well as curricular accreditation. Some institutions have sought and received either one or the other, or both.

It is not uncommon for private nonprofit technical institutes to offer a variety of curriculums. These most often are in the fields of the common technologies—mechanical, electrical, industrial, and civil. Some restrict their offerings to a single field but with curriculums at different levels of theoretical content. A few schools offer, in addition to curriculums at the technical institute level, programs of study for skilled craftsmen on the one hand or bachelor degree programs on the other, or both. When the institution offers programs of study in more than one discipline, each has a departmental chairman or head reporting to an academic dean. Schools offering instruction at different levels generally have a division for each level and a dean for each division. The hierarchy of academic control is through department head, divisional dean, dean of instruction, and president.

A typical organization structure for a private nonprofit technical institute is shown in Figure 1.

Proprietary institutions. The organization and administration of proprietary technical institutes frequently is simpler and more direct than that of nonprofit institutions. Some are corporate structures with boards of directors and others are privately owned and operated by a single individual or a small, closely-knit group. Many are quite small, with the owner-president having final responsibility for all phases of the total activity. He may delegate subject-matter control to instructional personnel but he rarely relinquishes business management of the enterprise to subordinates. He may do some teaching. At the other end of the continuum are several large enterprises with a central location and a number of branches or geographically separated operations. Such large schools normally exercise a rather rigid central office control over all phases of the activity. In between are many institutions which range from large to small, with the degree of personal direction by the president correlated inversely with the size of the operation.

A number of proprietary schools carry on excellent programs of instruction, but as a rule they place less emphasis upon fringe academic activities and concentrate on the core of technical content. The instructional staff members frequently carry heavy teaching loads, are specialists, have practical experience more imposing than their academic credentials, and enjoy but few of the fruits of faculty status. Almost inevitably these schools reflect the personalities, attitudes, philosophies, and convictions of their founder-owner-presidents whose life span may determine the life span of the school. In some ways these schools are more reactionary than their deficit-incurring endowed counterparts, and they tend to stick doggedly to a tried-and-found-true pattern of instruction. In other ways, however, they are quite liberal, unencumbered by a mechanism fraught with checks and controls; thus they can, by executive fiat, innovate on a moment's notice. As a consequence, they have at times initiated not only new curriculums but also instructional techniques which in due course are copied by the more staid educational institutions.

Some proprietary technical institutes carry on correspondence programs in addition to resident instruction. Often only minor refinements are required to offer through correspondence instruction the same curriculums offered on a resident basis. Such schools face

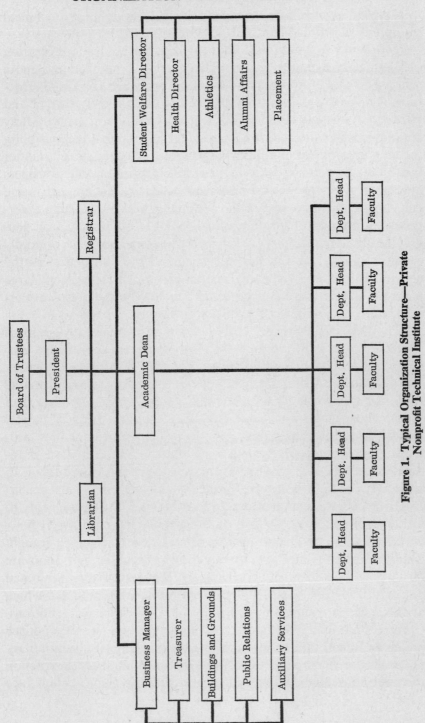

Figure 1. Typical Organization Structure—Private Nonprofit Technical Institute

a major challenge in trying to certify the maintenance of academic standards for correspondence students, but they try to meet this challenge by imposing rather rigid controls. Some even go so far as to require a short terminal period of residence for all correspondence students who wish to obtain a graduation credential.

Since profit is imperative for any proprietary enterprise, most of these schools have few peripheral academic activities. Student extracurricular activity is minimal. Teaching loads must be kept profitable and the individual teachers normally enjoy no more tenure than the average business employee. If enrollment drops off, teaching personnel must be cut back forthwith. These and similar conditions impose upon a proprietary school administration an unbelievable burden as it tries to maintain standards and still earn profits. Yet streamlined administrative staffs and hard-driving but ethical salesmanship have combined with good faculties to achieve excellence in many proprietary technical institutes. These contribute significantly to the total educational effort.

Technical Institute Divisions of Complex University Systems

The university attitude.   The history of technical institutes in the United States reveals that a considerable number of these institutions were led by one influence or another to transform themselves into conventional four-year engineering colleges. Such transformations have been occurring since the late 1800's. There is no valid reason why such changes will not continue. While the motives have been natural and largely above reproach, one cannot help but envision this future for each private technical institute now in operation. It seems that the greatest assurance one can have that a school operating technical institute programs will not abandon its objective and seek bachelor degree status is for it to be a large university which already has four-year programs in operation. Yet the vast majority of complex university systems have been slow to initiate technical institute curriculums.

Part of the reason may stem from a belief that two "kinds" of students in one institution make for internal morale problems. More realistically, the problems of organization structure and of distributing the total school resources are basic to such inaction. Then, too, a university administration may fear a possible loss of status if it departs from traditional bachelor and graduate programs. The same motivation, in fact, which causes technical institutes to "move up" to bachelor degree schools could cause a university to hesitate to offer technical institute programs. Whatever the reasons, not many universities have done so.

There are, however, notable exceptions. In 1931, Wickenden and Spahr listed the following accredited degree-granting institutions as being among such exceptions: Bradley Polytechnic Institute (Bradley University), Carnegie Institute of Technology, University of Idaho, and Iowa State College—all offering full-time day courses; in addition, Drexel Institute, Pennsylvania State College (Pennsylvania State University), Rutgers University, Washington University, and the University of Wisconsin offered evening courses either on campus or through extension divisions. But at that time Wickenden and Spahr believed the arrangement unwise. They thought it was better for the institution to "maintain one standard of admission, give one level of work, and award one grade of credential."[2] Time apparently substantiated this position, because in 1961 only one of the list offered accredited technical institute curriculums: Pennsylvania State University.

At the latter date, however, other large comprehensive universities had begun offering technical institute curriculums. Included among these were some large land-grant universities—Purdue University, Georgia Institute of Technology, the North Carolina State University, and the Oklahoma State University. A number of other large universities also were operating technical institute programs. These included Temple University, the University of Dayton, and the University of Houston.

The university structure. Each of these large universities is organized and administered in its own unique way to conduct its technical institute programs. There are, however, some common denominators. In each instance the chief executive of the university is responsible for all university activities. Fiscal, academic, and student welfare responsibilities are channeled through one route or another to him. While the technical institute entity may conduct its

[2] William E. Wickenden and Robert H. Spahr, *A Study of Technical Institutes* (Lancaster, Pennsylvania: Society for the Promotion of Engineering Education, 1931), p. 22.

affairs on a well-defined budget, this budget is a part of the total financial statement of the institution. Technical institute students are a part of the total student body and faculty members are a part of the institution's faculty. Student tuition and other incomes are collected by the institution and the disbursement of the university resources to the several subdivisions of it is, in the end, under the control of a central business office.

There are, however, many striking differences, especially among the state-controlled institutions. The Oklahoma State University conducts its technical institute program on the campus at Stillwater. Students use the same facilities as bachelor-degree candidates and participate in many of the same activities. In contrast, both the Georgia Institute of Technology and the North Carolina State University operate technical institute programs on separate campuses and under different names. The Southern Technical Institute, located at Marietta in suburban Atlanta, is the Georgia Tech program; and the Gaston Technical Institute—located in Gastonia, some miles from Raleigh—conducts the North Carolina program. Still a third organization structure is employed by both Purdue and the Pennsylvania State University. These institutions administer the technical institute curriculums through university extension divisions, operating centers in populous areas in their respective states. Both have main campus direction and some on-campus work, but the program is essentially an off-campus activity.

The large private university systems which include technical institute curriculums among their offerings probably have more similarities than their publicly controlled, tax-supported counterparts. The fact that they are not tax supported removes the obligation to meet the needs of people in a given geographical area; hence, extension divisions as such are not a part of their structure. At the University of Dayton the Technical Institute is administered by a Director who is responsible to the Dean of Engineering. At Temple University the Director of the Technical Institute has responsibility for technical institute curriculums under the Dean of the Community College and Technical Institute.

A condensed organization structure for a complex university system offering technical institute curriculums is shown in Figure 2.

Faculty and instruction.   The faculty members of technical institute divisions of large complex university systems, whether pub-

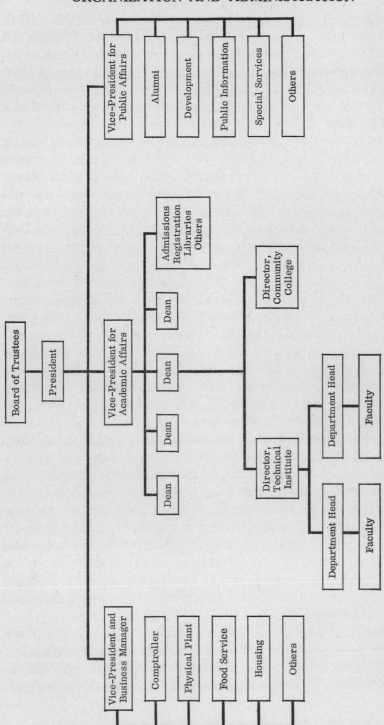

Figure 2. Condensed Organization Structure—Complex University Offering Technical Institute Curriculums

licly or privately controlled, normally enjoy the same conditions of faculty service as other faculties of the institution. Matters of tenure, teaching loads, participation in annuity and retirement programs, and similar prerogatives are uniformly administered. Academic rank and criteria for faculty promotion may deviate at times from regular norms, but the criteria used are judiciously determined and utilized. In some schools the technical institute faculty is used exclusively for the institute's own students; in others they teach broadly across the student body. Likewise, some schools isolate technical institute students in separate classes regardless of content, while in other schools students are intermingled in those courses common to both technical institute and bachelor-degree programs. The predominant practice, however, is to utilize a specialized staff to handle classes which are exclusively for technical institute students.

The level of teaching carried on in a technical institute division of a large university is definitely collegiate. Here, as elsewhere, level of instruction is difficult to measure and no generally accepted yardsticks are available. Certainly, many bachelor-degree programs include some content of minimal rigor and at times permit instructional techniques at variance with higher education standards. The same can be said of technical institute instruction.

Technical institute programs carried on by universities compare favorably with other programs at the same institutions. The faculty hold academic credentials adequate for their positions, though professional work experience is, at times, a requirement for a faculty appointment. Essentially, such programs are organized, administered and staffed according to the standards of each school.

The number of large universities offering technical institute instruction and the number of students enrolled is not large. At present the combined effort of all such institutions serves only a relatively small fraction of the total technical institute student body of the nation. The private nonprofit and proprietary technical institutes enroll a much larger fraction of the total. The universities, however, exert an extremely telling impact on the total movement. Having prestige, stability, and resources of both money and personnel, they automatically assume a leadership considerably beyond the point indicated by their enrollment. In general, such schools are cognizant of their role and are cautiously administered by competent educators.

The Publicly Controlled Local School

Technical institute curriculums are being offered in increasingly greater numbers by institutions which have their control lodged, in part or in whole, in local governments. Such institutions normally derive their major financial support from taxes levied by some municipal or county government, although tuition and privately contributed support may be significant. In some instances tax support is given by a state, by the federal government, or by both, but the control rests essentially in local hands. These schools fall into three groups: (1) municipal universities, (2) community-junior colleges, and (3) public school systems.

The local higher education institution. A limited number of municipal universities have inaugurated technical institute curriculums in recent years. These institutions are large complex university systems. Aside from the fact that they derive their major support from taxes levied on local government subdivisions, they are organized and administered much the same as any other university system.

An example of this type of institution is the University of Toledo. In addition to operating six colleges (offering bachelor degrees) and a graduate division, the University offers a number of curriculums in its Community and Technical College. These curriculums lead to an Associate Degree for completion of a two-year program. The College also offers university-parallel courses for students wishing to transfer to bachelor-degree programs. The institution is maintained by an annual appropriation made by the City Council and by student fees.

The University is governed by a Board of Directors and the chief executive officer is the President. Each of the colleges has a Dean. The Dean of the Community Technical College is responsible for all two-year terminal curriculums, which include programs of the technical institute type, as well as evening programs leading to certification in selected technical areas. Semester-hour fees are assessed all students; and nonresidents of Toledo are required to pay a higher fee. No specific facilities are identified for the College, but it has its own faculty. Students in all classes are on the same campus.

In general, the organization and administration of other municipal universities offering terminal technical curriculums are similar to those of the University of Toledo. Particular titles for both administrative personnel and for divisions of the institution may be different, but in substance the operation is the same. Programs are collegiate in level. Generally accepted conditions of faculty service are observed, and academic standards, physical plant facilities, library resources, student welfare services, and similar academic accoutrements are applicable to students in all classifications.

The community-junior college. As pointed out by Bethel and others:

> The community junior college is for all the people of the community. Therefore, it is concerned with the community educational needs at the college level. To meet these needs the community junior college is free to explore and determine its own educational objectives.[3]

To achieve the end goal of offering college-level education geared to community needs, many and varied local institutions have been established. Some are strictly local enterprises administered completely through the institution's own personnel with support derived from local taxes plus tuition. Some are joint enterprises of the municipality and some private agency such as the Y.M.C.A. Others are part of a system with some control and support coming from the county, the state, or the federal government. All may be classified as higher education.

Since communities themselves differ in so many respects, the community colleges also differ. Some community needs are universal, so that there is a common thread of similarity running through practically all community colleges. This is brought into focus by their attention to general education. It is, however, the unique community needs which emphasize the differences and which can be observed most readily in terminal curriculums. There are quite a number of these which are technical. Limited surveys have indicated that some 10–15 per cent of the more than 600 junior colleges of the country offer programs of the technical institute type.

New York State has systematically organized community technical colleges in several of the more populous areas of the state. These were created by the State Legislature; five institutions located in Binghamton, Brooklyn, Buffalo, Utica, and White Plains were

---

[3] Lawrence L. Bethel, Jesse P. Bogue, and Frank B. Lindsay, *Junior College Technical Education in Your Community* (New York: McGraw-Hill Book Company, 1948), p. 1.

designated in 1946. Subsequent legislation has stabilized the organization and structure of the system and provided an operational mode for all similar institutions in the state. In this system the state and the local community bear the cost of capital expenditures equally, and operating costs are split three ways by the state, the local community, and the students. Each school is organized independently with its own board, president, administration, and faculty.

Typical of these institutions is Broome Technical Community College located in Binghamton. The base for local tax support is Broome County. Students from outside the county pay a nonresident fee. A variety of two-year engineering technology and other terminal curriculums are offered. Some university-parallel work is given, as are short courses of interest and value to the residents of the community. The status of faculty members is good. The physical plant is well-designed. Students enjoy a well-rounded program of extracurricular activities. Some move on for further study to institutions granting the bachelor degree, but the majority go directly into productive employment upon graduation. Most of these students find employment locally. Broome Technical Community College, together with the other two-year colleges in the New York system, enrolled in excess of 19,000 students in 1962.

The community-junior colleges of the State of California are part of a system which differs markedly from the systems of other states. This difference derives in part from the philosophy of education pervading the thought of many California educators. This philosophy holds that community-junior college education is secondary, not higher, and that the thirteenth and fourteenth years should be integrated with, and be a continuation of, the prior program. Whether this is an upward extension of public school activity or a downward extension of college work into the traditional high school eleventh and twelfth year is not altogether clear. In either case, even though the junior colleges offer some university-parallel work, they are controlled to a significant degree by the State Department of Education. This Department not only has adopted regular policies for the support of junior colleges but also is empowered to prescribe regulations for administration and supervision. Faculty academic requirements are defined; building standards are determined; and library, laboratory, and other facilities are inspected and approved by the Department. The various junior colleges do enjoy a great deal of freedom, however; despite standards, regulations, and support, they are not regimented.

Insofar as curriculums of the technical institute type are concerned, the picture in the California junior colleges is clouded and quite difficult to evaluate by norms used in most other places. L. M. Jacobsen of the City College of San Francisco has charted the occupational-centered curriculums offered by the California junior colleges. Sixty-four colleges are included and the curriculums identified are placed in six groupings: (1) agriculture, horticulture, and forestry; (2) applied and graphic arts; (3) business and commerce; (4) trade and technical; (5) health service; and (6) other services.

The grouping entitled trade and technical lists 37 occupations. On the basis of titles only, 22 of these appear to be training programs for skilled artisans and thus are not within the purview of technical institute education. Such occupations as shoe repairing, welding and oxygen cutting, and furniture upholstering are among these. Fifteen of the 37 could be occupations requiring education of the technical institute type. These include the customary titles of electrical technology, industrial technology, communications, instrumentation, and the like. There are undoubtedly some fringe curriculums. Of those that appear to be of the technical institute type, there is no valid reason to suppose that all curriculums bearing the same title necessarily have the same level or content.

This can be gleaned from the publication *Education and Training for Technical Occupations,* published by the Los Angeles City School District as a guide for curriculum construction. A study of this publication reveals with some clarity the philosophy of integrated instruction through the high school, junior college, and university. A student may be "picked up" at some point in his education by a particular school and moved along toward his goal. In discussing the course requirements for design draftsman, the following recommendation is made for the junior college. "A high school graduate who has not completed the mathematics, drafting, and science required for this classification should have such courses available for him at the junior college level."[4]

Assuming that the Los Angeles approach to the problem is similar to that employed elsewhere in the state, the schools are doing a

---

[4] Donald D. Dauwalder, *Education and Training for Technical Occupations* (Los Angeles: Los Angeles City School District, 1961), p. 41.

magnificent job of fulfilling the objective of community colleges to satisfy the needs of people. The organization and administration of schools at all levels appear to require a blend of central regulation and individual school autonomy of the most delicate balance.

A number of other states have state regulations of varying degree for the establishment and maintenance of junior colleges. Some give financial support directly; others give through state colleges or universities. In some states funds are appropriated for certain junior colleges but not for others. Likewise, the emphasis placed upon curriculums of the technical institute type within the offerings of the schools themselves varies as widely as does the support received from the state. The differences found in the organization and administration of community-junior colleges in state systems are more numerous than the similarities.

This fact probably results from a multitude of growing pressures to resolve the problem of the great need for this type of technical education in the socio-economic milieu of the present industrial era. Community-junior colleges which have operated for many years are inaugurating terminal technical curriculums and new schools are being established for this purpose. That there is lack of consistency in what is being done is not necessarily a fault; it only serves to sharpen the focus on one of the most complex national problems of the time.

An examination of the founding of the Lansing Community College in Lansing, Michigan, will illustrate the point. As described in the May, 1960, issue of *Technical Education News:*

> Lansing Community College, one of 16 public two-year colleges in Michigan, was established expressly to train technicians for local industry and to provide occupational training for young people of the area. The college grew out of a request made to Michigan State University by the State Highway Department, Oldsmobile Division of General Motors, and other employers concerned with the shortage of people trained for their intermediate technical jobs.[5]

Approval to establish the college was granted in May, 1957, and classes began the following October with 225 full-time students. By 1960 the full-time equivalent enrollment was 542. Curriculums of the technical institute type in civil, electronics, and mechanical tech-

---

[5] "Technical Institute Profiles: Lansing Community College," New York: *Technical Education News* (May 1960), p. 7.

nology were offered the first year; nursing, business, and liberal arts programs were offered later.

Not all community-junior colleges are publicly controlled and tax supported. Some, such as Sinclair College in Dayton, Ohio, are operated as independent nonprofit institutions. This institution, established in 1887 by the Y.M.C.A. and servicing the community continually in a variety of ways, started engineering technology curriculums in 1954. It was separately incorporated in 1959 and, though housed in Y.M.C.A. facilities, it derives its support from tuition, gifts, and grants primarily from local industry. Having its own president and administrative personnel, it retains a full-time faculty and supplementary part-time staff drawn from the community.

The public school system.   The influence of Title VIII of the National Defense Education Act of 1958 upon public school programs for technicians has been great. Whether or not such programs are secondary, postsecondary, college level, or less-than-college level, they have been established and are operative.

According to the statute, funds appropriated for area vocational education programs are apportioned to the states by a pre-established formula. In order for a state to receive its allotment, it must spend an equal amount either from state or local funds. To be eligible to participate, the state must designate the state board as the sole agency for administering its program. In addition it must show plans, policies, and methods to be followed in the conduct of the program. The program itself must consist of one or more less-than-college grade courses conducted under public supervision and control. Such programs must be on an organized, systematic class basis designed to fit individuals for useful employment as technicians or skilled workers in recognized occupations requiring scientific or technical knowledge. It must be available to residents of the area who have completed junior high school or who are at least sixteen years old and can reasonably be expected to profit by the instruction offered.

Title VIII operations started in 1959, for which year $3,750,000 in federal funds were appropriated. In that year more than 250 schools in 49 states conducted programs for an enrollment of over 48,000 students. In 1960 all states plus the District of Columbia and Puerto Rico participated, with the number of schools and the number of students more than double that of the previous year. Institutions of many types participated. Vocational or trade schools made up the largest single category; comprehensive high schools and community or junior colleges were close behind.

In general, the content of programs developed reflects the study, experience, and findings of technical institutes which have been operating for many years. An examination of the content would lead one to conclude that the type of curriculum being offered should prepare technicians comparable to those being graduated by the established technical institutes of the country. This conclusion is subject to question, however, when one examines the administrative organization responsible for the operation at both the state and local levels.

State boards of vocational education are oriented toward the secondary vocational school objective. In most instances the administrative personnel on the local level are public school administrators, whose background of education and experience is directed toward the achievement of goals which differ from those of higher education. The objective of vocational technician training is to prepare adults for entry level employment in occupations which are defined as technical by industrial, scientific, commercial, and government agencies. This objective misses, as a rule, the higher education emphasis upon subject-matter competence and identification with a professional field. The overriding concern about instructional methodology and job competence tends to negate the higher education concern about the rigor of academic disciplines and the versatility to deal with unknowns.

It is not the purpose of this discussion to suggest that the vocational objective is unworthy, but an administration oriented toward the public secondary school, quite likely, will miss the purpose of technical education as that purpose is seen by individuals in higher education. The result probably will be the education of graduates who differ from the graduates of programs administered by persons in the field of higher education. The fact that both use the same terms to define their different activities only serves to make the dichotomy obscure and to build a semantic barrier between the two groups. Unfortunately, most educators find it extremely difficult to surmount this barrier. They become emotionally involved in an irrational, though loyal, support of preconceived meanings. The simple fact that the country needs lucid thought applied to this problem of developing first-rate technical institute programs is not likely to overcome this impasse.

There are some exceptions to this. At least two states, Illinois and Ohio, have started the development of a cooperative working relationship between the state boards and the engineering schools. The College of Engineering at the University of Illinois has designated a faculty member to work with the state board. Technical education conference-workshops have been cosponsored by the College of Engineering and the Division of Technical Education of the state. These are devoted to alerting the people who administer technical programs to the curriculum needs, laboratory requirements, and subject matter necessary to train high-level technicians.

In Ohio, where a well-ordered program has been established, a number of local school systems have organized curriculums in several technologies. These systems may work through the office of the State Supervisor of Trade and Industrial Education to secure the assistance of the deans and faculties of the engineering schools of the state. The intent in both states is to put into the public-school technical education programs the best that can be gleaned from both engineering and vocational education. It would be optimistic to conclude that the intent will be fully met, but the basis for cooperative guidance has been established. Perhaps this is a pattern of organization that will emerge eventually as the best for achieving the ultimate goals.

In summary, the technical institute program that is publicly controlled and local has great potential to make a significant contribution. With financial resources coming from the local, state, and federal governments, it has the wherewithal to conduct programs of great magnitude. No other educational agency could hope to match it. Whether or not such a program will gain acceptance hinges in part upon the willingness of the people to entrust higher education to secondary school administration, and in part upon the ability of secondary school administration to recognize the challenge with which it is faced.

Other Schools

There are a limited number of other schools offering education of the technical institute type. They do not fall within the categories so far identified, and they lack common characteristics which would identify them as a group themselves. Perhaps some of them should not be included even in the broad classification of schools offering programs of the technical institute type, yet each meets the principal criteria established for such programs.

One of these is Ferris State College, a part of the family of state colleges in Michigan. It was established as a proprietary school by W. N. Ferris in 1884 and became a state college in 1949. The purposes of the institution are met first by accepting students at their own individual scholastic levels and by holding fixed entrance requirements to a minimum. Students then are guided into those courses likely to give them the most desirable training for reaching the goal of vocational competency in the shortest practicable time. General education varies with the type of program pursued. High school trade courses and college preparatory courses, as well as several bachelor-degree programs, are offered. In addition, the school offers collegiate terminal programs for the training of technicians in various industrial, medical, scientific, and service-related occupations.

The institution is organized and administered by a board of control, president, deans, department chairmen, and faculty. There are also related offices for student welfare, fiscal, and physical plant control. The institution gains its uniqueness primarily from the clientele it serves. Age and previous educational experience are not limiting factors in admission and the institution takes pride in affirming its intent to give a second chance to students who have had previous unsuccessful school experiences.

Another of these schools, the RCA Institutes, is located in downtown New York. This oldest radio training center in the United States began in 1909 when E. E. Bucher organized a class in "wireless," according to a profile of the school published in *Technical Education News*.[6] It operated for a time as the Marconi Institute, and when the Radio Corporation of America was formed in 1919,

6 "Technical Institute Profiles: RCA Institutes, Inc.," New York: *Technical Education News* (October 1949), p. 5.

it became the Radio Institute of America and a part of RCA. The school has remained a member of the RCA family ever since, being incorporated under its present title in 1929. At present the institution retains a large professional staff and many laboratory assistants. The curriculums include a variety of vocational courses of various lengths and a two-year advanced technology program of considerable mathematical and scientific rigor.

The students come, to a large extent, from the surrounding geographical area, but there are resident students from every state and many foreign countries. They need not be employees of the corporation, nor are they guaranteed employment upon graduation. As would be expected, RCA takes more graduates than any other single company, but more than three fourths of them are employed elsewhere in the industry, frequently by competitors. The institution has excellent laboratories and its proximity to other corporation units permits use of industrial laboratories. Administration is placed in the hands of a board of directors composed of RCA executives, and a board of technical advisors keeps up-to-date inventions and practices in the course content.

Other industries have schools or programs of study which are also either totally or in part at the technical institute level. Unique among these is Westinghouse. Since the early 1900's, this industry's employees have participated in evening classes in a program heavily subsidized by the corporation. First-class instruction on a part-time basis with a part-time staff has produced many technicians, supervisors, and engineers for the electrical industry.

Northrop Aircraft (now the Northrop Corporation) established the Northrop Aeronautical Institute in 1942 to educate technical personnel for the aviation industry. The school utilized its own facilities from the start and offered instruction on a full-time basis. Enrollments grew rapidly and dormitories were erected to accommodate resident students. Programs of study were offered on a variety of levels from skilled mechanics to professional engineering. Entrance requirements equivalent to most colleges and universities have insured a uniformly well-prepared student body, and curriculums at the technical institute level have been rigorous. In 1953 the school achieved independent status and later changed its name to Northrop Institute of Technology. Although it now offers work leading to the bachelor degree in engineering, it retains the associate degree programs to educate technicians for the industry. One unique school operated by an industry is the Le Tourneau Technical Institute of Texas. R. G. Le Tourneau, President of R. G. Le Tourneau, Inc., manufacturers of heavy earthmoving equipment, established the school at the close of World War II, when the federal government released to him the Harmon General Hospital in Longview, Texas. The spacious facilities are used for dormitories and recreational areas as well as for class and laboratory instruction. Students spend half their time in school and half working in the industry. They may take secondary school work and then proceed to a junior college associate-degree program and ultimately to the bachelor degree. All programs combine work experience with study. Both are supplemented with a significant complement of social, religious, and cultural training. All applicants must furnish character references and, when enrolled, must attend regularly scheduled chapel programs. Students come from all over the country, are somewhat older than typical college students, and are employed after graduation by a variety of industries. In 1961, the institution reorganized as Le Tourneau College, which includes three divisions: the Technical Institute, the School of Aviation, and the School of Arts and Sciences.

In addition to those mentioned, a large number of other institutions offer programs of study at the technical institute level. The variety of administrative organizations, the range of purposes, the specific areas of academic instruction, and the particular clientele served is practically endless. *Technical Education News* in its series of Technical Institute Profiles has described many of these. Henninger, in his survey *The Technical Institute in America,* has made the most comprehensive tally of such schools. The Engineers' Council for Professional Development lists each year in its annual report all institutions having accredited curriculums. No single source identifies all institutions in the field, but publications such as these give a fairly comprehensive coverage of technical institute programs in the United States.

CHAPTER IV

The Content of
Technical Institute Curriculums

If the term technical institute is interpreted broadly enough, the content of technical institute curriculums can include a wide variety of subject-matter areas. In fact, any field of productive effort embracing professional practitioners on the one hand and skilled operators on the other presumably could have a middle liaison group of technicians. Engineering technicians, physical science technicians, and medical, biological, and dental technicians come readily to mind. It does not take much imagination to conceive of technician-level activities in business, in industrial production and operation, in manufacturing and institutional supervision, and so on. For each technician activity an educational program with its own particular content could be defined and a technical institute curriculum devised.

Up to the present such a broad connotation has not been used. The practice has been to recognize some rather uniformly applied limitation. As pointed out in Chapter I, the *Dictionary of Education* defines a technical institute as an institution "of higher learning offering instruction in one or more branches of *technology*. . . ."[1] Most of the literature in the field has placed emphasis upon engineering and the physical sciences, implying that the physical sciences are applied rather than pure. Since applied science is, in a sense, engineering, most technical institute curriculums are engineering-oriented. A discussion, therefore, of the content of technical institute curriculums should stress engineering-oriented programs, while recognizing that other orientations are possible.

---

[1] Carter V. Good, ed., *Dictionary of Education* (New York: McGraw-Hill Book Company, 1959), p. 554.

Curriculums with an Engineering Orientation

Curriculum criteria. In order to define engineering-oriented technical institute curriculums, it is important to define engineering. While there is no universally accepted definition of engineering, most authorities agree that there are certain concepts which are fundamental and must be included in any definition. Engineering is a creative profession. It employs the tools of science to design useful products from the earth's natural materials and to harness energy to do useful work. These tasks must be achieved through the guidance and direction of human effort, and must not exceed a cost someone is willing to pay. Above all, the entire professional organization must be cognizant of its public trust, must embrace the highest ethics, and must recognize that natural resources are God-given and not subject to willful exploitation. The technician who serves on the engineering team must, perforce, qualify to a degree in all of the above areas. The criteria which are used to define an engineering curriculum are in principle and in substance the criteria used to define an engineering-oriented technical institute curriculum.

Length of curriculums. Curriculums preparing persons for supporting roles in engineering are of shorter duration than curriculums preparing professional engineers. Most engineering curriculums are four academic years in length, although a number are five years. Technical institute curriculums vary from one year to a high of three years, with the vast majority in between. It would be incorrect to say that technical institute curriculums are, or should be, of two academic years' duration, although a two-year period appears to be the minimum for a program of genuine substance.

The two-year minimum, for example, has been adopted as one of the prerequisites for accreditation by the Engineers' Council for Professional Development, which is the recognized accrediting agency for technical institute curriculums.[2] In this instance, reference is made to two academic years without the specific requirement that two calendar years are needed. In fact, some excellent programs requiring less than two calendar years are accredited, but the instruction is given almost continuously without the traditional vaca-

[2] *Annual Report for the Year Ending September 30, 1962* (New York: Engineers' Council for Professional Development, September, 1962), p. 47.

tion breaks. It should be pointed out, however, that many educators find it difficult to compress the desirable content into two academic years.

Level of instruction. Instruction in engineering-oriented technical institute curriculums covers a spectrum of levels. The objectives of curriculums at the upper end of the spectrum closely approach those of engineering curriculums. At the other end the objectives approximate those found in secondary school programs in technical high schools. Between these extremes are gradations of both objective and level, so that it is almost impossible to distinguish exactly where a curriculum enters or leaves a so-called acceptable position.

This simple fact of difference in level has been the cause of widespread misunderstanding. Many individuals tend to lump all technical institute curriculums into one single band in the educational picture. Dr. Russell Beatty, President of Wentworth Institute, has attacked this position. He has been quite articulate in his identification of two levels of technical institute curriculums and of their graduates, who he classifies as industrial technicians and engineering technicians. Speaking to the American Technical Education Association, he said:

> There is still need for technicians to do the same scientific level of work that the technician did 25 years ago. At Wentworth Institute, we have chosen to call this kind of technician an Industrial Technician to differentiate him from the Engineering Technician. His mathematical background does not go beyond College Algebra and Trigonometry. His engineering science background is meager. He has a stronger shop practice and drafting background than the Engineering Technician. He is a very useful member of the technical team. But he is not an Engineering Technician.[3]

One is inclined to believe that Dr. Beatty has moved in the right direction but has unduly simplified a complex situation. He has focused attention upon the basic truth that all technical institute curriculums are not of identical level. It would appear, however, that rather than discrete levels of technicians and technical institute curriculums, there is a continuum. Differences between levels are hard to define, because each shades off almost imperceptibly to the levels above and below.

---

[3] H. Russell Beatty, *How the Technical Institutes Can Meet the Challenge of Technical Education* (Boston: Privately printed by the Wentworth Institute, 1958), p. 4.

In this connection, level itself is no index of quality. Some observers tend to assume that high-level programs are good and that lower-level programs are poor. Such an assumption is false, as has been so lucidly stated by McGraw in his study *Characteristics of Excellence in Engineering Technology Education:*

> The level of a program is determined by its objectives, and the quality by how well it achieves these objectives. If, for example, the objective of a program is to train retarded persons to perform simple household tasks, it may excel at accomplishing this objective. On the other hand, a graduate program in a highly abstract field may well be of poor quality.
>
> Some technical curricula intend to cover their subject matter at a level close to that of the engineering college, or at least that of the engineering college of a few years ago. Others set their objectives at essentially the same level of difficulty as the secondary school. Between these extremes we find a well-distributed range of objectives and levels.[4]

There is little question about the fact that each level of technical institute curriculums serves a valid purpose. The demand for technicians in industries reflects a need for capabilities which vary as widely as the levels of the preparatory programs. To cite one specific example, the Engineering and Construction Services Division of the Dow Chemical Company in Houston lists classifications from Grade Technical A through Grade Technical H in their Associate Program for engineering support personnel. For each of these classifications there are defined duties and responsibilities, minimum qualifications, and typical position titles. The range from laboratory assistant to design specialist spans all eight grades. Other industries classify technician personnel differently, but the fact remains that within the encompassing category of "technician" are many classification levels. That there is variety in the level of technical institute curriculums is to be expected. It is a natural outgrowth of conditions as they really are.

Mathematics. The critical content in defining level in any engineering-oriented technical institute curriculum is mathematics. It underlies true comprehension of the physical sciences which, in turn, are the foundations upon which the technical specialties are based.

---

[4] James L. McGraw, *Characteristics of Excellence in Engineering Technology Education* (Urbana, Illinois: American Society for Engineering Education, 1962), p. 13.

The technology studied will determine the content of the technical specialty, and there are differences in the required mathematical underpinning of the several technical specialties. Electrical technology probably places the greatest demands upon mathematical knowledge. Others vary slightly, while some, such as industrial technology, may place the emphasis on different mathematical concepts.

Selected topics from college-level algebra and college-level trigonometry are the first mathematics included in all technologies. From this point on, carefully chosen content from such areas of mathematics as analytic geometry, differential and integral calculus, differential equations, probability and statistics, vector algebra, and Boolean algebra may be required to support the technical specialty. It must be clearly understood that technical institute curriculums are not designed to be pre-engineering curriculums. Typical engineering curriculums devote at least two full years to a study of mathematics, basic science, and general education before any serious attention is given to professional courses. The depth of study and degree of understanding an engineering student must have of these fundamental subject-matter areas are thus considerably greater than can be expected from a technical institute student, who must cover the same areas in half the time. This is the reason for great emphasis upon the careful selection of topics to be included.

At all levels of education, the content included in the treatment of a particular subject is selected from the mass of knowledge in the field. Subjects rarely can be treated exhaustively. In designing the content of mathematics courses for the technical institute, the ultimate in consideration must be given to what the technology requires. For example, a program in electrical technology which concerns itself with the design of computers quite correctly could include some instruction in Boolean algebra. Such instruction could not be comprehensive because of the limited time permitted in a two-year program. The same statement can be made regarding the mathematics required in other technologies. In the longer professional engineering curriculums, more time is available for more inclusive coverage. As a consequence, the engineer has a broader base for the study of theoretical science and ultimately a greater reservoir of knowledge to use in design, development, and research. The technician with his more limited knowledge can go only so far. It is the mathematics which, in the end, determines just how far he can go. It is for this reason that mathematics is the key subject which determines the level of an engineering technology curriculum.

Science. Mathematics is not the sole determinant of curriculum level. The sciences also exert an important influence. Once mathematics is included, the level of a curriculum is defined by the comprehensiveness of the basic and the engineering sciences. Not only chemistry and physics (and in some curriculums, biology), but also statics, dynamics, fluid mechanics, electrical circuitry, material properties, and thermodynamics often are fundamental to the technical specialty. As was true in the study of mathematics, only selected topics can be included. These should be determined by the requirements of the technology and not defined by their more comprehensive counterparts in professional engineering curriculums.

The objective of the program in question dictates the nature and extent of its science inclusions. A curriculum in chemical engineering technology will include much more chemistry and the science of materials than one in industrial engineering technology. Even within the framework of a rather specific area, such as mechanical engineering technology, there may be particular curriculums which have more limited objectives. One curriculum might include heavy emphasis upon physics and thermodynamics, while another might lay stress upon statics, dynamics, and strength of materials. In structuring a curriculum, one works back from the final objective to the inclusions in the technical specialty and then to the required science. In this way the necessary topics to be drawn from the whole of science are defined. If the objectives are rather theoretical, the science inclusions will be quite comprehensive and the level will be high. Similarly, more practical objectives demand less scientific foundation, and the level will be lower.

The technical specialty. Important as mathematics and science may be in defining the level of a curriculum, they do not supply the content which in the end makes the technician. Since the common objective of all technical institute programs is to prepare graduates for supporting roles in engineering and science, the crucial content must be in the application of basic knowledge to practical problems. Where the professional must have breadth, the technician must have specialization. The professional should be free to call upon the specialized technical competence of several supporting technicians. Each of these quite rightly should have a more detailed knowledge in a narrower field. An industrial engineer can expect to be supported by a technician who is expert in time study. A mechanical engineer should look for competence in a tool designer. A research chemist might be critically dependent upon a technician who conducts experiments to determine the effects of radiation on metals and alloys. In all technological fields the technician supplies a high degree of special competence indispensable to the effective performance of the engineering team.

The precise content of a technical specialty cannot be defined once and for all, because it is always in transition. In today's swift-moving technology, innovations become established practice and move into obsolescence in a very brief span of years. Subject matter must be continually updated and techniques must be kept abreast of the times. All courses should emphasize the quantitative analytical approach. Content which is descriptive only may give a fine appreciation of the field but is of little value in preparing technicians who must come to grips with real problems. Technical specialties must be taught through both theory and practice. In most instances heavy emphasis should be placed upon laboratory work. The student must acquire intimate familiarity with apparatus, instrumentation, and techniques. He must be taught to collect, analyze, interpret, and present data. While being trained in a narrow field of specialization, he must be protected from meaningless repetition of routine activity. He is not earning a living but is in school to learn. Paradoxical as it may seem, the learning process must give maximum breadth to his narrow field. The laboratories, lectures, and recitations must be carefully integrated to achieve effective input in a limited time span.

The technical specialty also offers an opportunity to give the entire curriculum a unity, purpose, and meaning. The various segments of knowledge gleaned from the several subject-matter areas can be brought together in proper relationship, much as they will be in the work situation after graduation. Such cohesiveness, desirable in any program of study, is genuinely possible of achievement in the technical institute with its concentrated two-year interval.

The objective of the program defines the inclusions in the technical specialty. If the objective is to prepare technicians for work which is quite theoretical, then substantial science and mathematics courses must be included so that the level of the technical specialty may be high. It is not essential for this to be the case in order for the curriculum to be of genuine value. A technical specialty can be well-conceived, effectively presented, attain its goal, and still need little science support. It will be of relatively low level but its quality will be high. Regardless of level, the technical specialty is the crucial content of the total program and the important criterion in determining the general effectiveness of the curriculum.

The technical skills. One part of the technician's role in supporting the professional engineer requires him to serve as a liaison with skilled craftsmen. He must have sufficient capability to interpret the work of the engineer for the craftsman and the work of the craftsman for the engineer. In order to achieve such capability he needs specific instruction in the manual skills.

Traditionally, it was assumed that such capability was a requisite for the engineer himself. In more recent years, however, the great influx of theoretical science content has crowded out instruction in manipulative skills from almost all engineering curriculums. This widens the gap between engineer and artisan, making the need for liaison technician assistance imperative. It appears that in engineering education the emphasis upon theory will continue to increase, thus creating an ever-widening gap to be filled by the technician. Today, more than one echelon of technical assistance is required to transmit communications across the chasm between design and production. It is mandatory for technicians to acquire the capability needed to span this chasm.

Quite apart from their place in this liaison capacity, technical skills play a direct part in the work of many technicians. Drafting is an essential part of the work of technicians in design. Surveying is another activity which has a relatively heavy skill component. Technicians who work in chemical laboratories, electrical circuitry, time study, and many other fields utilize manual skills in some or many aspects of their work. The degree of such skill possessed by technicians contributes significantly to their worth.

In all technician fields the kind of skill required and the degree of perfection needed determine a definite part of technical institute curriculums. One responsible for developing curriculums must exercise care in determining how far skill training should go. A technician definitely is not a skilled artisan and a program designed to prepare such persons could not be classified as a technical institute program. However, the inclusion of training in certain skills does not make a craft program. Judicious selection of those instructional elements which produce in the student the correct kind and degree of skill is most important. As in all other subject-matter areas, care must be taken to insure compression of essential material into a minimum of time because of the brevity of the program.

Nontechnical content. The two-year engineering technology curriculum gives so little time for technical content which bears directly upon occupational competence that time devoted to nontechnical inclusions is reduced to an absolute minimum. Yet every responsible educator recognizes the need for such content. One must be on guard not to sacrifice some technical subject matter to make way for nontechnical courses and in so doing graduate individuals who are deficient in technical competence. Similarly, one must not go in the other direction and train technicians devoid of all formal instruction not tightly related to their work. Between these two horns of the dilemma, the technical institute educator struggles with the frustration imposed by an insoluble problem.

Engineering educators have faced a similar but less acute problem. Continually pressed to add more theoretical science subject matter, they have tried, however, to maintain a definite humanistic-social stem in all curriculums. This frequently results in the development of integrated courses which telescope longer sequences into brief but comprehensive coverage.[5] In spite of this, the engineering graduate frequently experiences insufficient breadth in his education. To follow a parallel practice in the briefer technical institute curriculums produces similar, more discernible deficiencies.

Many able technical institute educators have dealt with the problem of general education in engineering technology programs. The Committee on Institute Curriculums of the University of the State of New York published a bulletin in 1947 entitled *A Guide to the Development of Programs for the Institutes of Applied Arts and Sciences*. This bulletin stated that instruction in general fields is needed for the adequate personal, social, and occupational development of the individual. The *Guide* defined the nature and substance of this instruction by placing it in five areas dealing with (1) science and mathematics, (2) oral and written expression, (3) personal,

---

[5] *General Education in Engineering—A Report of the Humanistic Social Research Project* (Urbana, Illinois: American Society for Engineering Education, 1956).

social, and civic problems, (4) reading and other communication arts, and (5) personal and community health. It stated further that course material should be selected in a way that reaches freely across traditional subject-matter boundaries, and that every effort should be made to correlate it with the occupational objectives of the student. This concept of an integrated curriculum in which each subject matter reinforced the aims of the others was difficult to implement.

A few years later, the Board of Regents of the State of New York specified that students enrolled in two-year programs should earn 20 credit hours in communication, social studies, and the mathematics-science combination. This directive resulted in the inclusion of 2 three-hour courses in communications, two in the social science field, and the remainder of the 20 hours in mathematics and science. This shift prompted Dean Eskow of the Mohawk Valley Technical Institute to say in a speech in 1960:

> The two-year colleges are tending to move away from the vision of the founders. . . . When these men said coordination, they meant coordination. They most certainly did not mean giving the general education faculty 20 credit hours to use as they saw fit, and the technical faculty the balance of the time to develop independently, both groups working in splendid isolation, using different logics, ideas, and approaches.[6]

Not all educators are convinced that formal general education instruction is a requirement in a sound technical institute curriculum. This is particularly true of those associated with proprietary institutions. C. L. Foster, President of the Central Technical Institute, has stated the case for such schools with disarming frankness:

> None of the proprietary technical institutes feel unfriendly toward general education. We recognize the need for the expansion of moral, cultural, political, and economic subjects in our curriculums if we are to serve best the long-range needs of our collective society and the welfare of our nation as a whole. However, there are some reasons why technical institutes that depend entirely on tuition for subsistence are reluctant to add more general education to their curriculums.[7]

---

[6] Seymour Eskow, "A New Look At General Education," *Technical Education News* (June 1961), p. 7.

[7] C. L. Foster, "Nontax-supported Technical Institutes and General Education," *Technical Education News,* XIV, No. 1 (Fall 1954), p. 7.

Foster states some reasons for this position. (1) Such schools are inseparable from the industries they serve and would be criticized severely if added liberal arts courses would result in a noticeable decrease in the technical competence of graduates. (2) Students enroll in these schools because they offer the most expedient route to economic independence. (3) In these schools the faculties have many years of practical technical experience and feel that general education subjects are of minor importance. Foster takes the position that the formal educational program in an era of advancing technology is compelled to include the technical subject matter and that students, if properly encouraged, can pursue general educational courses after graduation.

This attitude toward formal general education in the engineering technology curriculum is shared by others not identified with proprietary schools. President Beatty of Wentworth Institute has stated:

> Most students now attending technical institutes have chosen this form of educational preparation rather than the liberal arts college program because they are more interested, at this particular time of their life, in the technical-vocational aspects of making a living than they are in the broader studies of man as a social, spiritual, and intellectual animal striving to perfect himself. . . . Therefore, it would appear to be better for technical institute educators to devote themselves to producing vocational competence in their students while this motivation is prevalent.[8]

Dr. Beatty also takes the position held by Foster regarding proper motivation for graduates to seek general education following their technical education. He also contends that much can be done informally to accomplish the objectives of a formal general education program. Extracurricular activities such as student councils, school publications, musical organizations, athletics, and laboratory courses can give experience which may be fully as broadening as formal courses in general studies.

On the whole, however, technical institute educators do support the position that a definite fraction of the curriculum should be devoted to formal instruction in nontechnical subject matter. Edward E. Booher reported a survey of general education in technical institutes at the 1954 meeting of the American Society for Engineering

---

[8] H. Russell Beatty, "The Place of General Studies in a Technical Institute Program," *Technical Education News* (May 1954), p. 15.

Education. The survey included 48 institutions and covered 249 curriculums. The average time devoted to general education was found to be 9.6 per cent of the total. The range extended from 0 to 35 per cent. Mr. Booher states, "In the 249 curriculums surveyed, we found these subjects in the following frequencies:[9]

Report writing, technical writing, and communication skills	169
Psychology and human relations	106
Social science survey and government	86
English grammar and composition	67
Public speaking	57
Economics	55

Henninger gives the median percentage of certain nontechnical inclusions in typical engineering technology curriculums.[10] If data relating to Communications, Humanistic-Social, and Physical Education and Health are drawn from his findings, they show the following:

		——— MEDIAN PERCENTAGES ———		
TECHNOLOGY	No. OF INSTITUTIONS	COMMUNI-CATIONS	HUMANISTIC-SOCIAL	P.E. & HEALTH
Electrical	13	11	13	0
Electronic	27	12	8	3
Mechanical	11	8	5	0

In summary, it can be said that the nontechnical content of engineering technology curriculums presents a major problem to many educators. The majority feel strongly that the limited time devoted to it is inadequate, but that the pressures from all sides combine to keep it restricted. First emphasis generally is given to communication skills, with some emphasis in the fields of human behavior, industrial economics, or government likely to be included. Unfortunately, course work in literature, art, music, language, history, philosophy, and similar subject matter is practically nonexistent.

Rigor. There are wide differences between similar curriculums

[9] Edward E. Booher, "Survey of General Education in Technical Institutes," *Technical Education News*, XIV, No. 1 (Fall 1954), p. 6.

[10] G. Ross Henninger, *The Technical Institute in America* (New York: McGraw-Hill Book Company, 1959), p. 48.

offered by many schools. The fact that course inclusions may be the same at two schools in no way reflects how rigorously the subject matter is pursued. Only a careful study of the topical breakdown of each particular course and an on-the-scene observation of demands made upon students can reveal the comprehensiveness and depth of coverage.

The institutions purportedly offering technical institute instruction deviate so widely from any standard norm that few uniform statements regarding all of them can be made. Probably no other segment of the educational structure embraces such a heterogeneous collection of schools. Among them are some of the finest giving excellent instruction in carefully designed curriculums. At the other end of the scale are disreputable institutions clinging to the coattails of a movement that is gaining momentum in the hope that they can ride along while exploiting unsuspecting students. To say that a curriculum is good or bad without placing it in the context of its total environment is meaningless.

The quality of an institution's faculty may determine whether or not a curriculum is effective. No amount of curriculum analysis or study can compensate for a weak faculty. The administration of an institution also contributes significantly to its achievement of goals. Because the whole technical institute concept is in flux, many conscientious educators find it difficult to acquire real understanding. Faculty members with genuine potential can be misled by unwitting administrators who find themselves assigned to a new and expanding facet of education. Administrators often can place the right words in the right places and still miss the total wholeness of a technical institute.

It is for these and other similar reasons that the curriculum alone is not an index of the accomplishments to be expected of students. It probably will be a long time before a satisfactory understanding of the term "technical institute" will be so widespread that it can be assumed that all educators know its meaning.

The curriculum as a whole. At present, no one person or group has the pre-eminence to define the ideal in a technical institute curriculum. Among the many pieces of literature on the subject, probably none is more authoritative than the McGraw Report of 1962. This was the report of a study sponsored by the American Society for Engineering Education and financed by a grant from the National Science Foundation. James McGraw, the project director, had a distinguished panel of experts to assist him, and the report was reviewed by almost 200 individuals qualified to evaluate some aspect of it.

That part of the report dealing with curriculum identifies three major areas of content: basic science courses, nontechnical courses, and technical courses.[11] A minimum length for any program is set at 60 semester credit hours, with the typical program being about 72 to 75. Minimum credit hours in the various content areas are defined. These, plus an illustrative program, are shown in Table 1.

TABLE 1

CURRICULUM SUMMARY IN SEMESTER CREDITS *

Basic Science Courses	MINIMUM†		ILLUSTRATION	
Mathematics (e.g., algebra, trigonometry, calculus)	9		12	
Physical Sciences (e.g., physics, chemistry)	6	15	6	18
Nontechnical Courses				
Communication (e.g., English composition, speech, report writing)	6		6	
Humanistic-Social Studies (e.g., economics, literature, history)	6		6	
Other (e.g., management, human relations, or additional humanistic-social studies)	3	15	3	15
Technical Courses				
Technical Skills (e.g., drafting-basic, manufacturing processes)	6		6	
Technical Specialties (e.g., semiconductors, strength of materials)	24	30	33	39
		60		72

* Taken from *Characteristics of Excellence in Engineering Technology Education* (Urbana, Ill.: American Society of Engineering Education, 1962), p. 25.

† Institutions should view with concern any curriculum which meets only the minimum shown above. Variations above the minimum are not only expected but desirable.

The report goes to some length to clarify the meaning of the term "curriculum." This is probably to caution educators against the

11 McGraw, *Characteristics of Excellence in Engineering Technology Education.*

tendency to compensate for the brief time span by dumping good but unrelated bits and pieces of content into the program. The report states:

> The term curriculum, as used in this report, connotes several ideas and distinctions which are important to any discussion of engineering technology curricula. First, a curriculum is an integrated sequence of organized courses. This would imply that a loose collection of courses, even though all are in a given occupational area, does not constitute a curriculum. Secondly, a curriculum is planned to fulfill a particular objective within a specified time. From this it follows that courses designed for a four-year program in engineering would not, in most cases, be appropriate components of a two-year program in engineering technology. The selection and organization of subject matter would be different, the time devoted to each subject would be different, and the emphasis of the curriculum and each of the courses in it would be different.
>
> . . . The more concentrated demands of time impose upon the engineering technology curriculum a greater need to integrate the courses with each other and to aim the subject matter more directly toward the particular demands of the specialized occupational field. This means that individual courses must usually be designed specifically for the engineering technology curriculum. Only if this is done can a balanced program with adequate coverage of the material be achieved within the time period.[12]

Another authoritative source of information regarding curriculums of the technical institute type is the United States Office of Education. A series of publications from the office of the Assistant Commissioner for Vocational and Technical Education are designed to provide information to help the states organize and operate programs under Title VIII of the National Defense Education Act of 1959. Two publications are available regarding each technology: mechanical technology, electrical technology, chemical and metallurgical technology, and so on. The first of these deals with suggested techniques for determining courses of study; the second presents a suggested two-year post-high school curriculum.

Some technical institute educators with engineering backgrounds would contend that this material is not genuinely designed for engineering technology curriculums because it is job-oriented. This position is reinforced by a statement made by W. M. Arnold in the foreword to the publication on suggested techniques:

---

[12] *Ibid.*, p. 22.

Each publication in this series indicates how job analysis and job relationship techniques can be used to facilitate the planning of training programs. Each publication contains the following information and suggestions:

1. General information about a technology or broad field of work.
2. A procedure for determining the relationship among jobs in order to develop homogeneous groups or clusters of occupations for which training may be given.
3. A method for determining the courses of study required to prepare students for a cluster or group of closely related occupations or for a specific occupation within a group.[13]

The heavy emphasis upon jobs and job clusters and the lack of identification with a professional field are not typical of higher education. Job analysis techniques and related training programs customarily are part of the vocational education complex. Also in the foreword to a volume on course outlines and curriculums, Arnold says, "Although the indicated level of instruction in this suggested curriculum is post high school, the sequence of course work may well start at any grade level where students have the prerequisite background and understanding."[14]

Yet these publications are unquestionably designed to assist in the education of engineering technicians, for in this same statement Arnold says, "Technical personnel in the modern industrial complex must have broad training in established fields of technology. Mechanical technology is one of those fields. All of the activities that support the work of the mechanical engineer require knowledge and understanding on the part of the engineer's team."[15]

The publication on Mechanical Technology presents a 72 credit-hour curriculum for a major in design. The curriculum is shown in Table 2. This publication also devotes considerable space to the clarification of the term "curriculum." It defines curriculum parameters and the objectives to be met. It emphasizes that all curriculums should be designed to provide maximum technical instruction in the time scheduled. In regard to structure, it states:

13 *Mechancial Technology Design and Production,* Suggested Technique for Determining Courses of Study in Vocational Education Programs, OE–80014 (Washington, D.C.: U.S. Government Printing Office, 1962), p. iii.

14 *Mechanical Technology Design and Production,* A Suggested 2-Year Post High School Curriculum, OE–80019 (Washington, D.C.: U.S. Government Printing Office, 1962), p. iii.

15 *Ibid.,* p. iii.

TABLE 2

MECHANICAL TECHNOLOGY
DESIGN MAJOR
(72 CREDIT HOURS)

Course No.	Course Title	Class Hours	Laboratory Hours	Total Hours	Credit Hours
FIRST YEAR					
First Term		16	9	25	18
G 100	Orientation	1	0	1	0
DP 103	Materials of Industry	3	0	3	3
DP 104	Mechanical Drafting I	2	6	8	4
DP 113	Manufacturing Processes I	2	3	5	3
M 115	Mathematics I	5	0	5	5
G 123	Communication Skills	3	0	3	3
Second Term		14	11	25	18
A 132	Technical Reporting	2	0	2	2
DP 133	Manufacturing Processes II	2	3	5	3
DP 134	Mechanical Drafting II	2	6	8	4
M 144	Mathematics II	4	0	4	4
S 145	Mechanics and Heat	4	2	6	5
SECOND YEAR					
Third Term		12	15	27	18
A 204	Strength of Materials	3	2	5	4
D 205	Basic Mechanisms	2	9	11	5
S 214	Electricity	3	2	5	4
G 222	American Institutions	2	0	2	2
S 223	Hydraulics and Pneumatics	2	2	4	3
Fourth Term		11	15	26	18
D 223	Machine Design	3	0	3	3
D 234	Basic Tool Design	1	6	7	4
D 235	Design Problems	1	9	10	5
G 283	Psychology & Human Relations	3	0	3	3
A 293	Industrial Organization and Institutions	3	0	3	3

A —Auxiliary or supporting technical courses
D —Specialized courses (Design Major)
DP—Specialized courses common to both design and production majors
G —General courses
M —Mathematics courses
S —Science courses

Taken from *Mechanical Technology Design and Production* (Washington, D.C.: U.S. Office of Education, 1962), p. 4.

Functional competence in a broad field such as mechanical technology has at least three components around which the curriculum must be structured: (1) the training should prepare the graduate to take an entry job in which he will be productive; (2) the broad,

TABLE 3*

			MECHANICAL TECHNOLOGY DESIGN MAJOR	McGRAW ILLUSTRATIVE CURRICULUM
BASIC SCIENCE COURSES				
Mathematics			9	12
M	115	5 cr. hrs.		
M	144	4 cr. hrs.		
Physical Science			12	6
S	145	5 cr. hrs.		
S	214	4 cr. hrs.		
S	223	3 cr. hrs.		
NONTECHNICAL COURSES				
Communications			5	6
A	132	2 cr. hrs.		
G	123	3 cr. hrs.		
Humanistic-Social Studies			5	6
G	222	2 cr. hrs.		
G	283	3 cr. hrs.		
Other			3	3
A	293	3 cr. hrs.		
G	100	0 cr. hrs.		
TECHNICAL COURSES				
Technical Skills			14	6
DP	104	4 cr. hrs.		
DP	113	3 cr. hrs.		
DP	133	3 cr. hrs.		
DP	134	4 cr. hrs.		
Technical Specialty			24	33
DP	103	3 cr. hrs.		
D	205	5 cr. hrs.		
D	233	3 cr. hrs.		
D	234	4 cr. hrs.		
D	235	5 cr. hrs.		
A	204	4 cr. hrs.		
Total			72	72

* U.S. Office of Education Curriculum in Mechanical Technology-Design Major, broken down into major content areas defined by McGraw. (Content breakdown by author.)

technical training, together with a reasonable amount of experience, should enable the graduate to advance to positions of increasing responsibility; and (3) the foundation provided by the training should be broad enough so that the graduate can do further study within his field of technology.[16]

It is of interest to examine a U.S. Office of Education curriculum when this curriculum is broken down according to the major areas defined by McGraw (see Table 1). Such an analysis of the Mechanical Technology-Design Major is shown in Table 3.

What a technical institute curriculum ought to be and what it really is are not always the same. In an effort to keep abreast of what curriculums are, the Technical Institute Division of the American Society for Engineering Education has a committee examining this topic at all times. In 1958, this committee reported to the Society on changes made in curriculum structure in the eight-year time span from 1949 to 1957. H. H. Kerr, then chairman of the Curriculum Development Committee stated, "We ascertained changes made in the last eight years in the number of contact hours devoted to five areas of study—basic sciences, technical specialties, allied technical specialties, administrative and managerial subjects, and general subjects."[17] The results of this study are shown in Table 4.

Accreditation and recognition. Accreditation practices in regard to higher education have included two areas of concern: institutions and curriculums. In the United States there are six regional accrediting associations accepting responsibility for institutional accreditation. Each differs from all of the others in organization, administration, policies, and procedures, but each adheres to essentially the same standards in approving colleges, universities, graduate schools, junior colleges, and other levels of higher education. They lack uniformity, however, in policies relating to the accreditation of specialized institutions, of which group the technical institute is a part.

In 1958, the National Commission on Accrediting called to the attention of the six regional associations the differences in these policies. The Middle States Association of Colleges and Secondary Schools and the Western College Association had established policies permitting accreditation of postsecondary specialized institutions. The North Central Association of Colleges and Secondary Schools and the Northwest Association of Secondary and Higher Schools adopted permissive policies broadly similar to the other two.

---

[16] *Ibid.,* p. 3.

[17] H. H. Kerr, "Curriculum Development Committee Report," *Technical Education News,* XVIII, No. 1 (Fall 1958), p. 12.

TABLE 4

PERCENTAGES OF CONTACT HOURS DEVOTED TO FIVE SECTIONS OF STUDY*

	Year	Basic Science	Technical Specialty	Allied Technical Specialty	Adminis- trative Manage- rial	General Subjects
Electronics-Radio-	1957	15.17	70.3	7.94	1.82	4.77
Television	1949	15.0	74.5	5.0	0.75	4.75
Air Conditioning-	1957	14.35	45.6	27.7	2.25	10.1
Heating-Refrigera-	1949	22.0	43.0	20.0	9.5	5.5
tion						
Architecture-Build-	1957	16.85	38.0	34.65	3.02	7.48
ing-Construction	1949	19.0	57.0	14.0	4.0	6.0
Aeronautics	1957	10.6	67.1	13.27	0.65	2.38
	1949	23.0	57.0	17.5	0.8	1.7
Mechanical Tech-	1957	27.5	31.0	23.9	6.1	11.5
nology	1949	31.5	47.0	8.5	5.4	7.5
Industrial Electricity	1957	20.2	47.1	18.42	2.94	11.3
	1949	23.0	53.0	13.1	3.1	7.8
Steam-Diesel-Auto-	1957	20.7	36.8	33.2	3.53	5.77
motive	1949	25.0	47.0	21.0	4.5	2.5
Civil	1957	16.42	63.75	12.15	0.20	6.5
	1949	21.0	50.0	16.0	6.0	7.0

The 1949 percentages used in this comparison were taken from a curriculum analysis made several years ago by Carmine Master and Kenneth Hammond, then students at Milwaukee School of Engineering. Their study, *Qualitative Analysis of Subject Matter in Technical Institute Type Curriculums as Accredited by the Engineers' Council for Professional Development on November 1, 1949,* was based on 49 accredited curriculums, representing 19 schools.

The 1957 percentages cover 109 ECPD-accredited curriculums, representing 35 schools.

* Taken from *Technical Education News,* Vol. XVIII, No. 1, Special Issue, 1958, p. 12.

More recently, the Southern Association has adopted certain policies regarding the accreditation of special-purpose institutions.

In general, the regional associations require specialized postsecondary institutions to demand high school graduation or the equivalent for admission, and to offer a core of general education. They will examine only schools which operate as nonprofit institutions.

The commission on institutions of higher education of the Middle States Association probably has devoted more time and attention to the accreditation of specialized schools than any other group. The commission has come to grips seriously with the problems surrounding the inclusion of a core of general studies in technical curriculums. The widespread establishment of technical community colleges offering technical institute curriculums in the Middle States area undoubtedly has stimulated this effort.

In meeting this situation, the Association has not shirked its responsibility. In April, 1956, it published Document No. 3.17, *General or Liberal Education in the Programs of Specialized Schools.* The document holds that a specialized school necessarily has a double objective. While recognizing that the first obligation is to produce competent specialists, the document argues that the development of vocational competence alone lacks intellectual depth and cultural breadth, characteristics essential in all types of higher education. The Association does not demand that specialized schools become *quasi* liberal arts colleges or that they should annex a collection of liberal arts courses to a specialized curriculum. Rather, an institution should work out its own balance between general and technical courses, taking into consideration the demands of the technical field and the necessity for individual development.

In a subsequent document, No. 4.60 published in December, 1958, the commission attacks the problem of balance between general and specialized courses again:

> The cue to a decision lies in each institution's own objectives. If they are strictly vocational, as they have every right to be, they imply concentration on producing a higher technical proficiency than a divided course can in the same length of time, or doing so more quickly. If they encompass intellectual breadth and personal enrichment as well as practical training, they pose an acute issue for a technical junior college. It obviously has to produce capable technicians, but in aspiring to collegiate status it necessarily accepts also the responsibilities for broader development which are common to all higher education. The problem is how to do both.[18]

This document also deals with the question of what kinds of courses should be counted as general education in a technical curriculum. It points out that professional usefulness should not be the criterion. Rather, it should include those courses which have the

---

[18] *Junior Colleges and Community Colleges,* Document No. 4.60 (New York: Middle States Association of Colleges and Secondary Schools, December 1958), p. 2.

best chance of drawing the student into important new areas of intellectual experience, of increasing his participation in his cultural heritage, and of preparing him to make sound judgments. The document emphasizes that courses whose purpose it is to develop communication or computation skills are not to be included among general education courses.

The Middle States Association has published an open letter to a college president. F. Taylor Jones, Executive Secretary of the Commission on Institutions of Higher Education, wrote the letter in answer to the question, "How does a community college earn accreditation?" In part, the letter states:

> Middle States evaluators never arrive with a check-sheet in their hands. They have no pattern to which a college must conform, no formula by which to rate it. The Middle States Association is interested, in essence in three questions:
> 1. Have this college and those who direct it clear and realistic concepts of (a) its functions, and (b) its educational objectives for its students?
> 2. Does the college have the educational programs, the human resources, the professional competence, the facilities, and the community support it needs to perform its functions and achieve its objectives, and to continue to do so for a reasonable time?
> 3. Is the college staff continually developing and correcting its program in the light of a sustained self-appraisal of its product, and requesting and receiving from its governing board the resources it needs to serve the community with constantly increasing effectiveness?
>
> When the answers to these questions are an unqualified "yes," accreditation follows as a matter of course. More important than that, the college will have made itself a strong and significant unit in our educational system.[19]

In addition to the regional accrediting associations, there are other special groups engaged in accreditation in the United States. The American Medical Association accredits medical schools; the American Association of Collegiate Schools of Business accredits business schools. Some professional societies have concerned themselves specifically with the accreditation of curriculums. This is true

---

[19] "How Does a Community College Earn Accreditation? An open letter to a college president from F. Taylor Jones, Executive Secretary of the Commission on Institutions of Higher Education.

of the Engineers' Council For Professional Development, which accredits engineering curriculums, and of the American Chemical Society, which accredits curriculums in chemistry. In all these instances educators associated with the fields being examined and the professional associations of the practitioners in the field have a voice in the accreditation. Since technicians do not compose a professional group and do not have any sort of organization, there is no technician association to function with the technical institutes in an accrediting activity.

For the many decades of technician education prior to World War II, no one set standards of excellence or content for technical institute curriculums. The wartime demands for technicians stimulated educators to think seriously about the problem. The National Council of Technical Schools, made up predominantly of proprietary institutions, established criteria for membership in its organization, but never seriously concerned itself with accreditation. The Council also represented only a fraction of the total number of technical institutes in the country. Other less comprehensive groupings of schools were formed, but they exerted little or no influence upon technical institute curriculums.

Thus, through the years technical institutes were established and developed curriculums independent of any genuine standard or guide. As a consequence, some schools developed curriculums of outstanding quality while others were satisfied with make-shift programs. No person could find one single source of information about the quality of technical institutes. This situation was the cause of great concern to many schools, particularly those which took pride in their efforts and which recognized the need to give honest guidance to the public in general.

In view of the facts that the most frequent programs of study offered by the better schools were engineering-related, the Society for the Promotion of Engineering Education (now the American Society for Engineering Education) was asked by many technical institutes for guidance. It was recognized that this society could assist only in engineering areas; however, this association with an established organization produced tangible effects in many schools. The society itself established a technical institute division in 1941. This offered a forum for discussion and a sounding board for proposals deemed useful to all such schools. Earlier, a movement had been set up by a group of technical institutes to organize their own accrediting agency, but the schools lacked the stature to give real meaning to accreditation and the movement failed. Had it succeeded, the accrediting activity could have been so devised that not just engineering but all types of programs could have been examined.

In 1940, a number of schools offering technical institute programs petitioned the Engineers' Council for Professional Development (E.C.P.D.) to inaugurate a program of accreditation for technical institute curriculums. After thorough study of the problem, E.C.P.D. set up a committee representing various kinds of institutions engaged in such work. Dean H. P. Hammond of Pennsylvania State College had done a substantial amount of the preparation for this activity and was named the first chairman. The Committee announced in 1945 that invitations to examine curriculums would be accepted.

Insofar as procedure is concerned, the rules laid down in 1945 have remained essentially the same through the years. The group actually was a subcommittee of the committee responsible for the accreditation of engineering curriculums. A special delegation of experts was named to visit each institution requesting accreditation and to report its findings to the subcommittee. A recommended action was reviewed by the parent committee and a final decision made by the council. The procedure has proved a trifle cumbersome and slow, but it must be remembered that in the beginning each decision made was a precedent-establishing action.

A diverse assortment of schools was permitted to apply. This assortment included endowed technical institutes; state, municipal, or federally supported technical institutes; Y.M.C.A. schools; junior colleges (public or private); extension divisions of universities; training programs and schools associated with industries; proprietary schools; denominational schools; and correspondence schools. Each school was to enunciate its purpose clearly and, if the purpose fell within E.C.P.D. defined limits, the evaluation of quality would be within the framework of such purpose. Except for the fact that it no longer accredits correspondence curriculums, E.C.P.D. has maintained to the present its policy regarding the type of school which may apply.

The subcommittee defined certain curriculum characteristics, standards, and accrediting principles to guide the work of examining committees. These were all published and have been carried in each annual report of E.C.P.D. The report for the year ending September 30, 1963, incorporates all modifications made since the original pronouncements and is a good guide for schools interested in initiating technical institute curriculums.

The small number of institutions seeking accreditation has been disappointing. The list of schools having accredited curriculums is carried in each E.C.P.D. annual report. Although the number of schools has not always been the same, it has never reflected a genuine, uniform acceptance of the curriculum accreditation idea. The 1962 annual report lists only 32 schools. In 1957, however, Henninger found 144 institutions offering curriculums considered of technical institute character.[20] This was significantly more than the 69 reported by Smith and Lipsett in 1954.[21] If the growth rate continued on to 1962, then at least 200 such schools would have been in operation. Perhaps not all would have had curriculums meeting E.C.P.D. criteria, but certainly the number would exceed 32.

Why then has this accreditation program been poorly received? No one knows the answer to this question, but certain conditions in society unquestionably contribute to it. First, the fact that there is such an accreditation program is not well known. Almost every student and employer is aware of the fact that schools are accredited, but in general this knowledge is with reference to institutional accreditation. If a school—for example, a junior college—has institutional accreditation by a regional body, its technical institute curriculums are deemed acceptable. Few laymen outside educational circles are aware of or concerned about curriculum accreditation. Thus, there is little public pressure upon a school to secure accreditation of the technical institute curriculum.

Second, students, their parents, industrial employers, and many educators have but scant knowledge about technical institutes. Knowing little about such schools, many have been suspicious of all of them, accredited or not. The question about accreditation has seldom been asked.

Third, employers and students alike have been quite indifferent to the fact of curriculum accreditation even when the fact is known.

---

[20] Henninger, *The Technical Institute in America*, p. 4.
[21] Lee F. Smith and Laurence Lipsett, *The Technical Institute* (New York: McGraw-Hill Book Company, 1956), p. 39.

If the government and private industry were to concern themselves about such accreditation at the time of employment, technical institute graduates and, in turn, the institutions would place great store upon accreditation.

The technical institute needs some yardstick of excellence, and sooner or later accreditation will be invoked uniformly. The accreditation machinery of E.C.P.D. is designed and operating. Many of its original imperfections have been eliminated. Insofar as engineering-oriented curriculums are concerned, it can function with genuine validity.

Curriculums Which Are Not Engineering-Oriented

Scope. When the term "technical institute" is broadly conceived, it embraces a wide range of activities, not all of which are engineering-oriented. People engaged in these activities function in a liaison capacity between professionals and skilled craftsmen. They must acquire a body of knowledge comprising both theory and practice as well as general education, but at a less than professional level. In a word, they are technicians.

Content. Curriculums designed to prepare these people for productive employment are structured in basically the same manner as engineering technology curriculums. Each has a component which bears directly upon the work to be done after graduation— the specialty. Each needs supporting subject matter to make comprehension of the specialty possible. There is always some degree of skill to be mastered. If the program is to be a genuine part of higher education, an appropriate inclusion of general studies is mandatory.

In each instance the program must be tailored to particular needs. The student, when graduated, will become a part of a group which has ways of doing things, patterns of thought, and ethical and philosophical guide lines that make it what it is. These all have a bearing upon the curriculum. It would not be possible to lift a curriculum from one area of endeavor and plant it in a dissimilar, though parallel, area. Each, however, can be analyzed, structured, and fitted into the particular program. The approach to curriculum construction does not deviate significantly from the approach used in constructing a curriculum in engineering technology.

Need. As time passes, the need for emphasis upon formal curriculums to educate technicians in nonengineering fields should increase. Knowledge in all fields is increasing, and the technician's job becomes more sophisticated. The time is rapidly passing when one can acquire all the needed preparation for technician assignments through the learning-by-doing apprenticeship of the past. The basic requirements of the technician's job must be compressed into a manageable curriculum. The professional in almost every field is moving up and away from the artisan, and the gap left between them cannot be filled by depending upon chance to produce a technician. The need for programs of the technical institute type in many nonengineering fields is a genuine one.

CHAPTER V

Technical Institute Faculty

The faculty is the heart of any educational institution and determines significantly the extent to which an institution fulfills its purposes. This is especially true of the technical institute, whose objective lies somewhere between that of the trade school and the college. Because of the rapid growth of this type of education following World War II, relatively few faculty members had a background of technical institute education. The faculty grew as the technical institute movement progressed. It probably could be said that the movement and the faculty were both products of a time and condition.

A small number of technical institutes had roots going back many decades, so that a nucleus of faculty was solidly based in the traditional pattern of such schools. But the overwhelming majority of faculty members participating in the growth of this activity came from widely divergent backgrounds, so that what finally emerged, or is still emerging, is new and different. As time passes and fluid conditions become more stabilized, definitive characteristics of the new technical institute faculty—the heart of the institution—become more easily discernible.

Faculty Characteristics

The relationship to other kinds of faculties. The technical institute faculty is not the same as an engineering school faculty. There are similarities between them, since both concern themselves with the same fields of endeavor; yet the end product of the curriculum—the technician—is not an engineer, and effort exerted to make him one detracts from the purpose of his education.

All professional education is, to a degree, terminal; that is, it ultimately reaches a point at which its students are pronounced ready. In engineering, however, employment after graduation is only part of the goal. The curriculum is so devised and the teaching is so oriented that continued formal study to attain graduate degrees is as much a part of the curriculum goal as is professional employment. In the technical institute such duality of purpose is practically impossible. The limited time of the curriculum prohibits this kind of luxury. In mathematics alone time eliminates comprehensiveness of coverage to a degree which confines instruction to that background considered optimum for the technical specialty. A graduate who wishes to pursue postgraduate study requiring advanced mathematics would be forced to retrace his steps and supplement his learning with those topics which had been by-passed. The same thing could be said of other fundamentals.

It is for this reason that the technical institute faculty member must be on guard against the understandable desire to pursue some segment of his subject matter to depths which are not required. In so doing, he may divert time from some other segment essential to the technician's proficiency. The purpose of the technical institute is not to prepare a student to carry on at a later date to the baccalaureate degree. If it were, the technical institute program would be a pre-engineering program. To understand this point and to gear instruction to the goals of the technical institute require a faculty which is not an engineering school faculty, but rather a technical institute faculty.

Similarly, the technical institute faculty is not a trade school faculty. Here again there is a parallel but not an identity. The technician must be taught certain skills, and frequently the person most qualified to teach them is a craftsman. It would be incorrect to state that there is no place in the curriculum for craftsmanship and no place on the faculty for a craftsman, but the development of artisans to the journeyman level is not the purpose of a technical institute program. A person teaching the technical skills must be cognizant of the place of such skills in the total educational effort. He must recognize that the technician must have an understanding of the craftsman's job. This enables the technician to give a precise interpretation or deft guidance to the engineer. His teacher need not put the technician through an apprenticeship training. Instruction of this kind beyond the needed amount may deprive the student of other instruction which must be placed in the tight curriculum. In addition, teaching the required mathematics and sciences is not the same as teaching the related shop mathematics or shop physics of the vocational program.

The technician's needs go beyond those of the journeyman, since he executes his work by calculations and analytical judgments rather than by rote or rule of thumb. Although a technician need not have comprehensive instruction in the derivation of mathematical equations, he must deal quantitatively with analysis and synthesis. To comprehend this total complex involving instruction in the skills themselves and the proper balance in instruction which supports the technical specialty demands a technical institute faculty, not a vocational school faculty.

In addition to these points, the faculty must understand the concept of engineering technician education as a part of the total system of higher education. Typically, the faculty identified with secondary education places heavy emphasis upon the mechanics of operation, teacher preparation in professional education courses, synthesis of subject matter into job-related components, and similar matters. This is not quite the same as a college-level faculty, which emphasizes the professional orientation of students, rigor of underlying concepts, and more advanced faculty preparation in subject-matter areas.

In addition, there is an all-pervasive attitude in higher education which is difficult to articulate but which is nonetheless critical. It presupposes maturity and significant individual learning on the part of students. It assumes a community of scholars and an environment enriched by libraries on a more comprehensive scale than normally associated with a secondary or vocational school. In order for a faculty to grasp this difference, it needs a penetrating understanding which transcends the superficial ability to state the difference in words. The important point is that a technical institute curriculum cannot be taught appropriately by a secondary school faculty and achieve the ends it is designed to achieve; it requires a technical institute faculty.

College degrees and work experience. What, then, constitutes a technical institute faculty? What formal academic credentials are needed? What other preparation is desirable? What kind of person should a faculty member be?

The question of degrees is always important in any consideration of a college-level faculty. A common, though by no means universal, answer is that a faculty member should not teach up to his maximum educational level. That is, one who teaches in a baccalaureate program should have earned a master's degree as a minimum requirement, and so on. Using this yardstick, one teaching in an associate degree program should have earned at least a bachelor's degree. The McGraw Report suggests that 50 per cent of the faculty should have engineering degrees to give good balance to the technical specialty.[1] In certain subject-matter areas still higher levels of education on the part of the teachers are desirable. Mathematics would be one such subject. Physics, chemistry, the engineering sciences, English, the humanities, and social studies might be others. In subject-matter areas directly related to the technical specialty, the need for higher-level academic credentials could be debatable. Since these areas so frequently deal with up-to-the-minute professional practice, it might be more important for the teacher to have work experience than study at the master's level.

In teaching certain of the technical skills, such as machine-shop practice, it is questionable whether or not even a bachelor's degree is needed. What is required is knowledge of and competence in the skill, plus ability to teach. The degree, as a measure of faculty capability, has more significance at higher levels of education than at lower levels. A graduate program leading to the Ph.D. requires a faculty with Ph.D.'s—a faculty who also have done independent research. At the associate degree level, particularly in technical institute programs, the need is less acute. It is important that each teacher have a mastery of his field which is greater than the mastery he must require of his students. Such a cushion gives a richness, depth, and meaning to the instruction, which otherwise might be adequate at best, and skeletal or fragmentary under pressure from gifted and inquiring students.

Theoretical study which is too advanced could make a teacher useless in an engineering technology classroom. His interests might not be with the problems of the technician; therefore he would be unfamiliar with and unsympathetic toward this level of challenge. Such lack of sympathy focuses attention upon an essential quality in a good technical institute faculty member. He must be convinced

[1] James L. McGraw, *Characteristics of Excellence in Engineering Technology Education* (Urbana, Illinois: American Society for Engineering Education, 1962), p. 17.

that this level of education has a real value of its own. If he thinks that a technical institute program is a watered-down version of engineering, he will fail in his mission.

Unfortunately, such people have sometimes found their way into technical institute faculties. At times they undermine the confidence of students in their goals. That such an effect is achieved inadvertently does not lessen its deteriorating influence. Students can become dissatisfied with their program and thereby acquire a feeling of inferiority or of being secondary. They emerge as unhappy graduates, or perhaps abandon their education altogether. In contrast, a faculty member who believes in the program can transmit his enthusiasm to his students. This not only stimulates learning but also gives the graduate confidence that his role in society is important. No amount of formal education or practical work experience can compensate for a lack of enthusiasm.

Faculty Organization

Departmental faculties.   A common question about technical institutes concerns the structure of the faculty organization. Is it wise, for example, to have a single faculty group which teaches all subjects? Should the same person teach related but distinctly different courses? Should the faculty member who teaches machine design also teach mathematics and physics? Should he who teaches motion and time study also teach mathematics, accounting, and technical report writing? This approach raises the basic question: Is such a practice likely to improve or to reduce teaching effectiveness in a technical institute?

One may argue that such use of faculty improves the integration of subject matter. A teacher of electronics presumably knows what knowledge of mathematics is required, what concepts regarding the structure of matter are important, and so on. Carried to its extreme, this approach would result in using one experienced professional to teach all of the courses in the curriculum because he knows best what the job will demand. A complete integration of all disciplines thus would give the proper emphasis to important areas and keep all subjects in appropriate balance. It would produce a graduate carefully groomed to fit into his niche in the world of work.

Opposing this argument is the one which holds that the proper understanding of a subject results from independent study of it. In this regard, mathematics is a discipline which, though used as a tool by an electronic technician, is also an end in itself. A genuinely detached study of mathematics permits the student to move uninhibited to novel solutions of traditional problems and perhaps opens the door to entirely new concepts. Similarly, in other subject matter areas the yoke of professional practice is lifted, permitting each individual to see for himself the relationships which exist among the many disciplines included in the curriculum. While such an approach may fail to bring the graduate up to as high a level of proficiency for his entry job in industry, it raises his ceiling for long-range growth and encourages inquiry, open-mindedness, and freshness.

Between these extremes many combinations exist. It would be difficult to assess the merits of them all and to arrive at the one best suited for all technical institute programs. Certainly it would be impossible to prove that there is one best way if performance of graduates is the criterion. Each school produces some graduates who are expert and some who are ordinary. No system to date has been completely without merit or without blemish. A kind of middle ground between the extremes is most frequent. It is common for technical institutes to have faculties identified with departments and, at the same time, to permit certain faculty members to cross departmental lines to teach a course outside. Some degree of fluidity allows the institution to capitalize upon the capabilities of gifted teachers and frequently effects a financial saving through the efficient use of teaching personnel.

A review of faculty organizations at schools having accredited curriculums shows that departmentalization of faculty appears to depend in part upon the number of faculty members. The most frequent practice is to have a department identified with each curriculum area, plus a department of general studies and a science department. In such an organization, departmental faculties such as those in mechanical technology, electrical technology, and industrial technology would be responsible for courses in both the technical skills and the technical specialty associated with their particular technologies. A larger institution might break a technology faculty into more than one department and separate the several science areas and general studies areas into such smaller subdivisions as mathematics, physics, chemistry, English, psychology, economics, and so on.

Smaller schools have fewer departments, and some schools draw no departmental lines at all, even though some faculty members teach only in their own discipline.

The faculty member's assignment. The technical institute faculty member is a teacher. In most instances he does little or no research. Unlike his counterpart in many universities, particularly universities that include graduate programs of study in their offerings, he devotes practically all his effort to teaching. This is due in part to the fact that the students are not pursuing research projects in their programs; thus, there is no call upon the faculty member to direct such projects. Also, the laboratories and other facilities at technical institutes normally are not designed for research. But most important of all, the faculty member typically is not research-oriented himself. Relatively few technical institute teachers have pursued graduate instruction through the doctorate. Their work experience seldom is in research. In fact, most are attracted to the technical institute field because they wish to teach, and this is what they do.

Also, as teachers, they are called upon less frequently than high school teachers to give guidance and counsel to students. A relatively high percentage of technical institute students have stabilized their educational objectives. They are not in an exploratory program trying to determine career objectives. Rather, they have made this decision and are enrolled in an intensive program of study where teaching is what they seek. As a rule, the average age of such students is somewhat higher than that of college freshmen and sophomores. They are more serious, more diligent, more likely to be concerned if teaching is ineffective. As a result, the faculty member is constrained to look upon teaching—not research, publications, or counselling and guidance—as his job.

Teacher-student ratios are about the same in technical institutes as in most higher education institutions. The heavy emphasis upon laboratory work, with a limited number of stations for students in class, tends to keep the class size relatively low. In all other respects the factors which influence teaching loads are about the same. This applies to credit hours of teaching, lesson preparation, grading of examinations, and the like.

Academic titles and academic rank sometimes are the same as those in most colleges, but deviations are common. In a 1962 study,

Carson found 12 of 21 institutions surveyed used the traditional instructor, assistant professor, associate professor, and professor titles.[2] He also found such titles as assistant instructor, associate instructor, senior instructor, supervisor instructor, instructor 1, 2, 3, and 4, and lecturer. It is common for technical institute divisions of large universities to use titles employed in other divisions of the same institution. The single-purpose institutions more frequently deviate from the traditional practice. Some institutions—particularly private, proprietary technical institutes—may lump all teaching personnel into a single faculty without specific ranks or titles. There are variations in salary and, when rank and title are used, salaries are related to rank. Carson found in his survey that those schools using traditional ranks paid salaries for the academic year ranging from $3,600 to $7,250 for instructor; $4,800 to $9,200 for assistant professor; $5,580 to $10,500 for associate professor; and $6,300 to $13,000 for professor.

Faculty recruitment.   Technical institute faculty members come from widely divergent backgrounds. Henninger found that slightly more than half the institutions he surveyed reported that their average full-time teacher had a master's degree or equivalent graduate study.[3] Thirty-five per cent reported that the average teacher had the bachelor's degree. The average teacher at the remaining institutions had a lesser academic credential: high school diploma, associate degree, or technical institute certificate. The same survey revealed that at 86 institutions which reported industrial experience of faculty members, the median was between six and seven years.

There apparently is no source of faculty members which consistently supplies any given type or kind of teacher. A significant number come from former careers as high school teachers. Some have had prior experience teaching in college, especially in an engineering school. Many move directly from industry into technical institute teaching. Some follow a more devious route, going from high school teaching into industry and then to a technical institute faculty. A few go directly from college graduation into technical institute teaching. Those with a limited formal educational back-

[2] R. G. Carson, Jr., "Survey of Faculty Salaries in Techical Institutes," *Technical Education News* (November 1962), p. 14.

[3] G. Ross Henninger, *The Technical Institute in America* (New York: McGraw-Hill Book Company, 1959), p. 71.

ground invariably have pertinent industrial experience. A high school graduate may serve an apprenticeship and become a journeyman machinist. If he has the other needed qualifications, he can become a valuable member of the faculty. Experienced tool and die designers frequently have no formal college education but can bring to a technical institute instructional staff a rich background which would be difficult to duplicate with college courses. The technical institute graduate himself can supplement his qualifications with work experience, return to teaching, and be extremely effective. Some teaching assignments, however, demand advanced theoretical knowledge, and only the rarest of exceptions could hope to acquire it without graduate study.

Faculty development. In evaluating the total faculty, the contribution of each teacher must be considered. If, as a whole, the faculty can bring to the student body an abundance of practical "know how" plus a sound and comprehensive "know why," it is not necessary to demand that each person on the faculty possess this same balance individually. Each should have a genuine understanding of the total technical institute objective, however, and should see clearly the place of technician education in the total scheme of higher education. Since the overwhelming majority of teachers come to the technical institute without this qualification, a number of in-service training programs, short courses, and workshops have been sponsored by universities to give this background.

Graney has reported on one of the first of these programs, which was held at Purdue University in 1950.[4] This was a pioneering venture, the general purpose of which was twofold. The first objective was to bring together both administrators and teachers for an intensive study of the many issues then confronting technical institute education. The second was to make definite recommendations regarding the establishment of training programs for prospective teachers. These same themes were of concern to the New York State Education Department at the time the technical community colleges were being organized in the state. Pre-service and in-service programs of instruction for faculty members were held at Cornell University and elsewhere. Lawrence Jarvie, then Associate Commissioner of Education, in an article in 1948, stated:

---

[4] Maurice Graney, "Purdue's Summer Workshop Draws Cross Section of Technical Institute Personnel," *Technical Education News* (October 1950), p. 1.

If technical institutes are to become an important part of the pattern of higher education, thinking must go beyond just the matter of plant and equipment to the problems of type and quality of instructors. . . . In the preparation of instructors there are two points at which preparation must go on: first, at the pre-service level, and second, at the in-service level. The latter needs much greater emphasis than has been the case at most institutions in the past.[5]

Other programs for the in-service development of teachers have been held at the Oklahoma State University, Pennsylvania State University, and a number of other schools. Some of these, such as the ones under the direction of Dobrovolny at the University of Illinois and of Curry at the University of Houston, have been sponsored by the National Science Foundation and have given financial assistance to participants. Others which have had government support have dealt with specific problems in developing science areas. As an example, the Pennsylvania State University has held eight-week summer programs on Nuclear Energy for Technical Institute Instructors. These programs were sponsored jointly by the American Society for Engineering Education and the Atomic Energy Commission, and included a two-week program at the Argonne National Laboratory.

Such efforts unquestionably enhance faculty capability and presumably will be needed in the future to upgrade teachers who are recruited from industry and from high school and engineering college faculties. In a very significant measure the faculty contribution defines whether or not the institution achieves its objective. Bringing to the institution individuals who possess widely different but essential talents, and then giving them a sound technical institute orientation, may be the best way to mold an effective faculty.

---

[5] Lawrence L. Jarvie, "Preparation of Technical Institute Instructors is Challenge to Schools," *Technical Education News* (March 1948), p. 6.

CHAPTER VI

The Individual and
the Technical Institute

In the final analysis educational institutions and educational programs exist primarily for the purpose of educating individuals. So much is said and written about schools, curriculums, physical plant, equipment, faculty, administrative organizations, and similar topics that one easily could get confused about the ultimate purpose of education. Students get lost as individuals when they are referred to as freshmen, graduates, pre-meds, engineers, or drop-outs. In fact, the calloused attitude of today is reflected in the use of such expressions as teaching mathematics or economics, or teaching a class, a laboratory, or a seminar. Yet each individual is a person with feelings and ambitions, is perhaps gifted or mediocre, has his moments of heartache and triumph, and—probably most important of all—has given long and careful thought to what he should do and, in the end, has gambled his future on some particular educational program.

The individual who elects a technical institute program is just such a person. What prompted him to choose such a school? What can be expected when he is graduated? What will be his capabilities and limitations? What will be his role in the economy? What recognition can he expect from society? These and many other questions like them are pertinent to a discussion of the technical institute. Reasonably definitive answers can be given to some of them. For others the answers are hard to find, uncertain, and speculative.

In analyzing the individual and the technical institute, there are three broad areas of interest which must be explored: (1) Where do students come from, what kind of people are they, and what do they want? (2) What do they actually achieve in school and what is their place in industry? (3) Where do they fit into society and what recognition does society give to them?

The Technical Institute Student

In spite of the growing interest in technical institute students since World War II, there are surprisingly few factual data which define the kinds of individuals such students are. There is an abundance of speculation. While this speculation frequently comes from well-qualified authorities, it deals less with the subject of what technical institute students are than with what they ought to be. The definition of the student is clouded with inaccuracies and prejudices, but from it emerge certain generally accepted conclusions.

Two-year versus four-year programs. Most well-informed peoples are aware of the high attrition rate in four-year bachelor programs. This rate probably is higher for curriculums in engineering and science than it is for most other curriculums. The causes for college drop-outs are many and varied. A number of students are unable to sustain the financial burden for four years. Another group lacks the academic capability to cope with higher-level subject matter. Still others lack the motivation to sustain study for so long a period. There are also emotional and adjustment problems which cause students to terminate study before completion. The list of causes for disruption of study is practically endless.

A sizable portion of college withdrawals from four-year curriculums could have found satisfaction and achieved completion in a two-year program. Moreover, the completion of a two-year program which has some terminal aspects prepares a graduate more appropriately for gainful employment and a productive career than the half completion of a longer program. A four-year engineering program, for example, utilizes the first two years of study to prepare a student to carry on for the last two years. One who withdraws from such a program has little preparation to move into employment. The graduate of a two-year engineering technology program presumably is prepared to start work. His level of attainment is less than it would have been had he completed the four-year program, but this attainment is specifically employment-related, and the first two years of engineering are not.

Thus, it may be argued that some who are destined not to finish the engineering curriculum would have been wiser to enroll and finish the technical institute program. This would apply to those students who could not afford four years of study but could pay for two, and to those who experience difficulty with advanced theory. Since the theoretical demands of the technical institute are less rigorous than those of the engineering school, a number of people who wish to work in engineering fields, but who are more adept at handling applied theory than at pursuing abstract content, would be well advised to study in the technical institute.

Such statements should not be construed to mean that the technical institute should become the last resort of the poor and the inept. Individuals possess different levels of capability in many diverse areas, and those who are more gifted in advanced mathematics are not more worthy persons than those whose talents are in the application of theory of a somewhat less advanced degree. Who is to say which person is needed most or serves best? Certainly in a complex society many, many kinds of capability are important to the welfare of all. It is more appropriate to recognize and develop those capabilities an individual has than to encourage all to aspire to particular achievements regardless of aptitude, for in the end only the few succeed.

The individual and his interest. Another group of students who should study to be technicians rather than engineers or scientists is composed of those whose interest is in the technician's activity. Persons in this group may have abundant means for longer periods of study and may have unusually high capability to handle advanced mathematics. The simple fact is that they *prefer* the technician's job. It is, however, quite difficult to discover just who such students are. This is true for a variety of reasons, two of which are quite important.

First, most youngsters are not really sure just what it is they prefer to do. Frequently, only at maturity does an individual know which occupation interests him most. When the time is at hand to make a choice of schools, he is confused.

Second, many people who advise youngsters about careers do not always know just what the job of an engineer or scientist entails. Often a high school boy who is gifted in mathematics and physics is advised to study engineering. Certainly such a boy may have the capacity to become an engineer, but does he want to? Similarly, a high school boy may tinker with his father's power mower and may like to change the spark plugs in the family car. Someone will say he should be an engineer, and the young man may fasten on this idea with tenacity. But does he want to be an engineer?

It is not common for a student to be counseled to enroll in a technical institute program before he has tried for the bachelor degree. Advisers who are familiar with the technical institute objective apparently are hesitant to recommend to a good student a program of higher education which does not qualify him for the bachelor degree. Those who are unfamiliar with the technical institute are incapable of recommending it. Similarly, students themselves are unlikely to select a technical institute program as a higher education goal. Smith and Lipsett point out that on questionnaires many students unrealistically will list prestige occupations such as physician, lawyer, and accountant as career goals.[1] Even though they may not really prefer the professional field, they feel the social pressure for the bachelor degree. As Henninger has stated:

> This latter situation reflects one of the major problems which continues to arise to plague the technical institute idea in education. That is, the question of status—social status, if you please. This status question is inherent in the prevailing American habit of regarding a four-year baccalaureate degree more as a mark of social distinction than as a measure of the fitness and effectiveness of the educational program for the individual receiving it.[2]

The source of students.   These factors combine to make the four-year college, particularly the schools of engineering, an important source of students for the technical institutes. The question, in reality the problem, of transfers from engineering schools has been examined from time to time. It is generally agreed that if the transfer student is, in fact, a failure who wants to complete the engineering program but cannot, then the practice is undesirable. If, however, the student transfers as a result of counselling based on demonstrable aptitude and genuine interest, the practice not only benefits the student but also strengthens the programs of both the technical institute and the engineering school.

Unfortunately, too many who transfer are of the former kind and are regarded as failures by themselves and others. They are believed

---

[1] Lee F. Smith and Laurence Lipsett, *The Technical Institute* (New York: McGraw-Hill Book Company, 1956), p. 125.

[2] G. Ross Henninger, "The Technical Institute in America," *Journal of Engineering Education,* LI, No. 1 (October 1960), p. 33.

to be not good enough to become engineers, and erroneously are supposed to be good prospects for the technical institute. This engenders low morale among both students and faculty, who look upon the technical institute as a dumping ground for castoffs from engineering curriculums. Such an attitude is not consistent with the concept of the engineering team, and it constitutes a major problem in technical institute education.

In spite of the fact that in many parts of the country high school counselling does not emphasize technical institute education, high schools are the principal source of students. Henninger's analysis of student source of 97 technical institutes showed an average of 58 per cent coming directly from high school.[3] Of the schools analyzed, those which were publicly supported drew 67 per cent directly from high school, and the private schools drew 46 per cent.

Quite a number of students come to the technical institute from industry after a period of employment. Such individuals often start work immediately after high school and presumably see the difficulty of promotion without additional technical capability. The technical institute offers them the kind of intensive, short-term program which will improve their competence and open the door to more productive and more challenging work. This kind of student is more frequently found in private schools located in larger cities. Schools which offer part-time evening programs may have 100 per cent of the enrollment coming from industries where the students are fully employed in the daytime. It is not uncommon for such industries to pay tuition and other costs for employees, or to reimburse them for a part or all of such costs. Unfortunately, many of these part-time evening students complete only the technical content, particularly if it is closely related to their work. They tend to defer the general studies to a later time or omit them completely, thereby defeating one purpose of the curriculum.

Some student characteristics. Students entering technical institute programs average somewhat older than students entering four-year bachelor programs. This is obvious because many students enter after a period of work experience or transfer from other programs. A young man pressed for funds may work for five years before accumulating enough money to go to school. If during this time he

---

[3] G. Ross Henninger, *The Technical Institute in America* (New York: McGraw-Hill Book Company, 1959), p. 53.

has married and assumed sizable family obligations, he is eager to enroll in a two-year program so that he can return to work without a long delay. The prospect of a four-year program often is overwhelming, and so a much higher percentage of such people enroll in a technical institute than in engineering programs.

Henninger found that in a study of 93 technical institutes the average age at entrance ranged from 18 to 27 years.[4] Other less comprehensive studies support this finding, but show a tendency for resident students in small town schools to be younger than commuting students in schools located in larger communities. Of the same 93 institutions, Henninger reported that an average of 52 per cent of enrolled students completed their programs and were graduated.

In another study covering one publicly supported school, Hamm found that about 60 per cent of any given class was graduated.[5] How these data compare with data on program completion in four-year engineering schools is somewhat obscure. The engineering school drop-out rate is higher, but the program is longer. Scattered data on enrollments at the end of two years of engineering school are inconclusive but show about the same retention as technical institutes for the same time period. Hamm also reported that most of the technical institute students come from families in which the parents completed high school but not college. The students themselves usually were in the upper two thirds of their high school graduating classes.

Technical institute enrollments.   A survey and an analysis of the types of schools attended by technical institute students and the numbers in each have been made each year since 1945. While such analyses have not been exhaustive and have not always utilized the same sources for data, they give a good picture of the patterns of enrollments since World War II. These studies were first prepared by Leo F. Smith and were published annually in *Technical Educational News* until 1956.

Smith's first survey, published in June of 1945, showed enrollments for the academic year 1944–45. The 82 schools reporting were listed in four categories. These categories with enrollment totals for each are shown in Table 5.

---

[4] *Ibid.,* p. 58.
[5] "Data on Faculty and Students Revealed in Study of Broome County Technical Institute," *Technical Education News* (June 1956), p. 12.

TABLE 5

1944–45 TECHNICAL INSTITUTE ENROLLMENTS BY TYPE OF SCHOOL*

Type of School	Day	Evening	Total
State and Municipal	1,527	3,082	4,609
Privately Endowed	1,256	3,711	4,967
Proprietary	2,205	1,544	3,749
Maritime Academies State & Federal	5,550	0	5,550
Total	10,583	8,337	18,875

* According to Leo F. Smith in *Technical Education News,* Special Issue (June 1945), p. 1.

In 1947, Smith added two new categories of schools: extension divisions of colleges and universities, and Y.M.C.A. schools. The number of institutions reporting data dropped to 77, but total enrollments jumped to 29,138 for day students and 20,305 for evening and special students, giving a total of 49,435. In succeeding years Smith followed the established pattern until 1953, when he discontinued the state but retained the federal maritime academies. In 1955, he abolished this category altogether. The last survey conducted by Smith was for the academic year 1955–56 in which 71 institutions reported total enrollments of 67,163.

The Manpower Studies Committee of the Technical Institute Division of the American Society for Engineering Education (under the chairmanship of Donald C. Metz) also conducted surveys, starting in the academic year 1953–54. These surveys were concerned with engineering-oriented curriculums only, and thus tapped a somewhat different source than the Smith surveys, which were not limited in this way. Donald C. Metz reported these findings annually through A.S.E.E., and included statistics drawn from schools not necessarily identifying themselves as technical institutes but offering curriculums of this type. Metz also gathered data on graduates. He reported that 15,314 students graduated from 148 schools enrolling 64,722 in 1955–56. By 1961–62 the number of schools reporting had risen to 197 with enrollments of 70,199, but the number of graduates had dropped to 14,350.

Summary. It would be difficult to summarize, from the facts available, which students in the United States want technical institute education and what they would like such education to include. It is probably correct to state that significantly greater numbers want such education than the numbers enrolled indicate. The enrollments are low because the schools offer graduation credentials which lack status value and because there is confusion in the minds of both students and the public regarding the differences between engineering education and technical education. As a rule, students who are enrolled are somewhat older than average college students, are less interested in advanced theory than are engineering students, and believe they lack either time or money to finance a four-year program. They come to such schools directly from high school, transfer from bachelor programs, or enter after or during industrial employment. They are more interested in *what* and *how* than in *why,* and tend to pursue technical, job-related courses rather than general studies.

The Student's Achievement in School and His Place in Industry

The pace of technological development during the middle decades of the twentieth century drew statements from industry, from the government, and from education that the United States needed thousands upon thousands more scientists and engineers. Yet the results of most careful investigations to determine the specifics of such need revealed that it was not so much scientists and engineers but technicians who were in short supply. Such studies repeatedly emphasized the fact that the nation needed not more and bigger schools of science and engineering but better ones. More significantly, perhaps, they showed that whether or not more engineers and scientists were needed, there probably were not enough people with the necessary potential for such advanced education. Whether the country chose to like it or not, it would be forced to alter the traditional national pattern of education and utilize the manpower it had and might expect to have. The rate of increase in need for technical manpower so far exceeded the rate of increase in population that old concepts of manpower utilization would have to change. The nation could not continue to undereducate and misuse engineers and scientists. It would be forced to supplement their productivity with well-trained technicians.

The technician's job. In spite of this consistent finding, there was an amazing lack of agreement upon what properly constituted the work of the technicians. In 1957 a Task Force on Technical Institute Curricula was sponsored jointly by the President's Committee on Scientists and Engineers and A.S.E.E. It consisted of nine members under the chairmanship of Donald E. Irwin of the General Electric Company. Its purpose was to review the content of curriculums of the technical-institute type, obtain opinions concerning the adequacy of such curriculums, and make recommendations for improvement.

In reporting the findings of this task force, William G. Torpey, Executive Secretary, included some very penetrating and disturbing findings.[6] This was demonstrated by the wide variety of work done by persons classified as technicians as reported to the task force. This work ranged from duties usually assigned to mechanics to those usually assigned to graduate engineers. Torpey also reported that the respondents from 96 industries replying to the task force did not seem to know, in terms of specifics, what actually should constitute a satisfactory technical institute curriculum.

In spite of this lack of knowledge about what should be in the curriculums, many made pointed comments casting doubt upon the adequacy of the curriculums offered. Some 46 per cent of the respondents thought the education was only reasonably complete, while an additional 18 per cent were strongly critical. Many felt additional training should have been given to the students while in school, and the overwhelming majority (79 per cent) stated that it was necessary to provide further training in the company before the individual could perform his technician duties satisfactorily. After analyzing the evidence obtained, however, the task force concluded that a curriculum containing a high proportion of mathematics, basic sciences, and laboratory techniques, and a smaller amount of specialization, was favored by employers. Perhaps this was so because a large segment of employers felt that the curriculums of many schools failed to keep abreast of latest industrial developments. To help improve the total situation, the task force recommended that industry be encouraged to develop a more uniform understanding of the content of a technician's job and to foster programs of better communications with technical institutes. The general tenor of these findings was supported by others both before and after the task force survey.

In 1945 Mark Ellingson reported a study of 394 graduates of a

---

6 William G. Torpey, "Adequacy of Technical Institute Curricula," *Journal of Engineering Education*, L, No. 2 (November 1959), p. 131.

three-year cooperative electrical course. After these graduates had been on the job some 10 to 15 years, 11.9 per cent were classified as assemblers, inspectors, and testers, while another 18 per cent held engineering positions doing design and research. He stated that the evidence showed a wide distribution of jobs into which graduates went, both as to level and area.[7]

In 1954 Dean C. J. Freund of the College of Engineering, University of Detroit, commented on the place of the technician in industry. It seemed to Freund that the most significant feature of the relationship was that the vast majority of engineers did not understand the function of the technicians. Commenting on this point, he stated:

> In spite of the serious shortage of technicians, and the fact that too many engineers spend much of their time on technicians' assignment, I suspect that 90 per cent of our engineers never give thought to the education of technicians. I further suspect that 90 per cent don't even know that the technical institute is the proper educational institution for the preparation of technicians.[8]

Commenting on this same point in 1955, W. Scott Hill held that it contributes to industry's inability to get maximum utilization of technician personnel. According to Hill, engineering groups were reluctant to revise their practices to the point where work was broken down into various professional levels and the proper utilization made of those with less than four years of training.[9]

Any penetrating study of the place of technicians in industry will disclose the fact that an accurate analysis of job activities is obstructed by the lack of uniformity in job titles. This is an understandable situation, since industries tend to employ titles traditionally associated with and descriptive of particular activities. Some activities become modified by technological improvements but retain the accustomed title. This is particularly true of the older, well-established industries, the operations of which have spanned a number of revolutionary scientific breakthroughs. There are, however, many new industries spawned in recent years by new discoveries; these

---

[7] Mark Ellingson, "Technical Institute Graduate's Place in American Industry," *Technical Education News* (January 1945), p. 1.

[8] C. J. Freund, "The Technician and the Engineer," *Technical Education News,* XIII, No. 4 (June 1954), p. 11.

[9] W. Scott Hill, "GE's Recent Experiences in Hiring Technicians," *Technical Education News,* XV, No. 1 (1955), p. 4.

have created a whole new cluster of job titles. At times it is difficult to determine just what common elements exist in job activities carrying widely different titles. In addition, it is not uncommon to alter the title a person may have, although the activity itself remains unchanged. This may occur because a new title lends greater prestige to the job; employment categories at times are as subject to fashion as are other human endeavors. All of these factors combine to confuse the answer to the question: What jobs do technicians hold in industry?

Henninger lists 14 representative curricular areas and hundreds of typical occupational titles for graduates of these areas.[10] This list includes such time-honored names as "survey party chief" and "design draftsman," as well as such imprecise titles as "installation specialist" and "laboratory assistant," and also a number of glamorous new names such as "guided missile technician." The Department of Labor study of technical occupations for science and engineering support personnel (published in 1961) uncovered numerous job titles which trigger the imagination—for example, "nuclear research laboratory technician," and "technical plastics specialist." Other investigators have scrutinized industry and found technicians employed in every conceivable area of activity. The only conclusion one can reach is that every segment of industrial enterprise is open to technicians and their place in the aero-space age is critical.

The technician as a supervisor. A number of industrial employers have seen in the technical institute graduate a person prepared for and capable of supervisory work. In view of the fact that he has only a limited schooling in theoretical subject matter, he has a definite ceiling upon his advancement in creative design and research. In order to move ahead in such areas he must acquire more knowledge through either intensive self-study or formal education. The likelihood of achieving such knowledge is quite remote for two reasons. First, the typical technician is one whose primary interests are not in theoretical study and research. Had they been, he probably would have pursued such study early in his educational career. Second, after he has worked as a tehcnician for a while, his personal responsibilities generally are of a magnitude that would make serious advanced study extremely difficult. In either case,

---

[10] Henninger, *The Technical Institute in America*, p. 198.

advanced study is unlikely and his upward movement in purely technical fields is improbable. In supervision the situation is quite different; a modicum of technical background frequently is a great asset, but comprehensive theoretical education is seldom a necessity and generally is of less importance than other qualifications. A technical institute graduate who has acquired some pertinent work experience and who possesses the basic personal qualifications is well prepared to move into supervision.

It is relevant to note that characteristics which industry defines as desirable in any competent technician are also those commonly thought desirable in a supervisor. One statement regarding the characteristics which industry regards as basic for a good technician was made by Kimball C. Cummings of the Minneapolis-Honeywell Regulator Company.[11] He enumerated seven characteristics: (1) education, in which special emphasis should be given to mathematics, science, shop practice, and the technical specialty; (2) experience; (3) general ability, which Kimball has defined as mental ability somewhat above average; (4) engineering aptitude; (5) ability to get along with others; (6) thoroughness; and (7) responsibility and drive. All these qualifications are also important for a supervisor in industry. As a consequence, technicians move into and up through the ranks of supervision and administration.

In the opinion of some industrialists, the technician is a better risk for supervision than the engineer. Frank J. Johnson of the Lockheed Aircraft Corporation made this observation in an article published in 1954.[12] According to Johnson, the graduate engineer often is overtrained for starting supervisory jobs and may be spoiled by the number of positions and high starting salaries offered him at the time of graduation. Johnson argued that the technical institute level of training is one of the answers to industry's supervisory problem. It utilizes intensive courses which are adaptable to the needs of industry to give the graduates a practical know-how. More important, perhaps, the graduate is not as spoiled by job offers and appears willing to start at the bottom rung of the supervision ladder.

The technician and the engineering team. The articulation

---

[11] Kimball C. Cummings, "Characteristics of the Technician as an Engineering Aide," *Technical Education News*, XVI, No. 1 (1956), p. 11.

[12] Frank J. Johnson, "Technical Institutes Can Train Supervisors for Industry," *Technical Education News*, XIII, No. 4 (1954) p. 14.

between technicians on the one hand and engineers and scientists on the other, and between technical institutes and engineering colleges, has been the subject of comment by a number of writers. In an article published in 1961, Irving L. Kosow lamented the fact that the status-seeking society of the United States continues a hierarchy of education programs that separates the technical institute from the engineering school.[13] In fact, he envisioned a widening gap between the two as engineering education became more heavily science-oriented, unless some action was taken to bridge the chasm between these two types of engineering institutions of higher education. He proposed a first year of technical institute study composed of broad academic courses paralleling, but less rigorous than, the first year of a pre-engineering curriculum. At its conclusion a student could transfer to a four-year engineering program or be better prepared to make the most of a more specialized technician-training second year. In the latter, the second year would not be overly specialized in any case. In this way the movement of students either way between the two programs would be more fluid and more individuals would be induced to pursue programs commensurate with their real capabilities.

In his article Kosow quoted Lillie and Stockwell, who contend that highly specialized technical institute curriculums of necessity will have to be broadened, thereby permitting transfer to baccalaureate programs without undue loss. Lillie and Stockwell stated further that such a trend already was discernible and that several leading technical institutes have provided additional work leading to a bachelor's degree.[14]

W. G. Whipple of the Westinghouse Electric Corporation took a different point of view in an article published in 1962.[15] He stated that most technical institutes have patterned curriculums after broad-based university programs, with the result that they give watered-down bachelor degree education. By doing so they have failed to offer the unique type of education which is needed by

13 Irving L. Koskow, "A Proposal For Increased Articulation Between Technical Institutes and Engineering Colleges," *Journal of Engineering Education*, LII, No. 2 (November 1961), p. 116.

14 J. Lillie and R. E. Stockwell, "A Local Problem for Engineering Education," *Junior College Journal* (October 1960), p. 16.

15 W. G. Whipple, "What Does Industry Expect of Technical Institute Graduates?" *Technical Education News* (April 1962), p. 12.

persons in many industrial jobs, which specializes in training that teaches people how to do things, and which fills the void created by the drift of engineering education away from the art and toward the science of engineering. Whipple maintained that industry expects and needs technical institute graduates qualified and willing to go into (1) engineering design work, (2) manufacturing and production fields, (3) sales, and (4) service. He did not go so far as to want technicians trained for particular jobs, but he opposed a common program at the first-year level for both engineers and technicians.

The relationship of employment of engineers, scientists, and technicians by industry was the subject of an article by Bernard Michael, Bureau of Labor Statistics, published in 1962.[16] In his article Michael analyzed the survey "Scientific and Technical Personnel in Industry, 1960," made by the National Science Foundation. He found that the number of technicians employed in industry in 1960 was 8.1 per cent higher than in 1959. The total was broken down into four occupational groups: (1) draftsmen; (2) engineering and physical science technicians; (3) medical, agricultural, and biological technicians; and (4) other technicians.

The engineering and physical science technician group showed an increase of 13.7 per cent, largest of any group. Although all major industries utilized technicians, more than two fifths were employed in electrical equipment, telecommunications and broadcasting, machinery and aircraft firms. Some interesting facts regarding ratios of technicians to engineers and scientists were noted. Food, textiles and apparel, and construction showed an increase, while motor vehicles and aircraft showed a decrease in the ratio. Scientists and engineers were found to be present in higher concentrations in large companies—5,000 or more employees—than in smaller companies. Technicians, while following a similar employment pattern, were found in highest concentrations in the large companies of industries with complex and advanced technologies. Industries with the heaviest concentrations of scientists and engineers in research and development also used large numbers of technicians in that area, but no such industry employed more technicians than engineering and

---

[16] Bernard Michael, "Statistics for 1959 and 1960 Include Research and Development," *Technical Education News* (January 1962), p. 1.

scientific personnel. About 27 per cent of all technicians were engaged primarily in research and development activities.

Some specific examples.   A penetrating analysis of what technicians do on the job was included in a conference held at Iowa State University in 1962. This conference, conducted at the request of the Office of Emergency Planning of the Executive Office of the President of the United States, brought together 56 leaders of industry and education to examine many aspects of engineering technician manpower.[17]

At the conference C. J. Draker, T. A. Gedicke, and John A. Greenlee reported on what engineering technicians did at the Collins Radio Company. At Collins, technicians took the engineers' ideas, given verbally or as limited sketches and schematics, and put them into physical form. Such form was achieved as engineering drawings for manufacturing personnel, or as prototypes. The technicians needed manual skills to operate hand and machine tools as well as a thorough knowledge and understanding of electronics. They required a strong background in mathematics, including calculus, for their design calculations. They worked regularly with transistors and other semiconductors and were required to have intimate familiarity with pulse systems, UHF, and microwave techniques. They used many kinds of electrical test equipment and submitted technical test reports. They were required to visualize, to have inquisitive and retentive minds, and to understand the principles of design. Last, and by no means least in the competitive electronics industry, they had to realize fully the serious economic implications of their work.

At the same conference Ray A. Engle of the Fisher Governor Company described the activities of technicians employed by his company. In design engineering, graduate engineers determined the parameters for major projects or products. As soon thereafter as feasible, the design, layout, detailing, calculations, standardization programs, procurement and testing of prototypes, testing of final products, and report writing were assigned to technicians. In research, technicians tested prototypes, performed tests for quality control, made stress analyses and systems analyses, and in general utilized the equipment normally available in a laboratory. Inasmuch as products manufactured by the company covered a wide range of

17 "Proceedings of the Conference on Engineering Technician Manpower," *The Iowa State University Bulletin,* LXI, No. 20 (October 17, 1962), p. 25.

items, technicians were required to use considerable independent judgment. Since the technicians had to communicate with men in almost every department, it was essential that they have high-level communications capability. In general, the technicians needed traits similar to those of professional engineers, with one exception: depth of theoretical knowledge. Since their work made use of known principles and physical laws, they were not involved in basic research or extremely high-level theoretical procedures.

These reports at the Iowa State University Conference and kindred reports from other employers of engineers, scientists, and technicians sharply focused the attention of the nation upon the achievements of technicians in the economy of the United States. As new materials are developed and as new industrial processes become more complex, the problem of building products which give an improved performance and are characterized by greater reliability becomes increasingly difficult. Likewise, the problem of meeting continually rising costs of both material and labor, and at the same time providing high quality products at competitive prices in the domestic and world markets, demands the most efficient use of manpower at all levels. While industry will continue to need more and better engineers and scientists, these people can be productive only if they are free to do the creative work which their long education has prepared them to do.

The engineering technician has proved to be the major release valve which can permit the free flow of such high-level effort into channels where it is most needed. He can continue to function in this way, and to do so with increasing effectiveness, if his true achievements are recognized and he becomes available in adequate numbers. This fact undoubtedly prompted the following comment by the Department of Labor in its Manpower Report to the Congress in 1963:

> The extremely rapid growth in technician occupations is another noteworthy trend, which is expected to continue. Although the shortage of engineers and scientists—and the consequent need to relieve these professional workers of tasks which can be performed by less highly trained persons—have helped to increase employment of technicians in the past two decades, the growth of these occupations has a more fundamental cause. It is due basically to the increasing complexity of modern technology, which has created a need for workers who have some basic scientific and mathematical

knowledge and also specialized training in some aspect of technology.

In 1960 the number of technicians working with engineers and scientists was about 775,000 according to a rough estimate. It is anticipated that, during the next 10 to 15 years, demand will increase at least as fast in these occupations as in engineering and the sciences, leading possibly to a doubling in requirements by 1975.[18]

Summary. It appears then, in summary, that though technicians make an almost incalculable contribution to industrial enterprise, their place in the total scheme of things is not well-understood either by employers or by engineers and scientists whose work they support. Employers are not clear about just what technicians are supposed to do, and engineers are slow to adjust their own activities in order to utilize technician assistance efficiently. Both engineers and employers are ignorant of and critical of technician education. In spite of these facts there are places where the potential contribution of technicians has been recognized and utilized. As technology continues to become more complex, more of such recognition and utilization will take place. A closer integration of educational programs and a more intimate interlacing of technical and engineering functions in industry will emerge. Inevitably, more technicians will be educated and used in industry because of the intrinsic value of their achievements.

The Technician's Recognition by Society

The general scene. One of the paradoxical aspects of the culture of the United States has been that most people speak with great pride of their capacity to work, but they seek an education which will reduce the amount of work they must do. Professional people are held in high esteem in part because of the misconception that somehow their greater education reduces their need to labor. The muddled notion of status is a bewildering maze of education, ignorance, idleness, and work. Out of all this have emerged the status symbols which are recognized by every school child. The clothes or uniform a person wears on the job, the size of an office or the depth of the carpet, the lunchroom in which one eats, the door he enters,

---

[18] U.S. Department of Labor, *A Report on Manpower Requirements, Resources, Utilization and Training* (Washington, D.C.: U.S. Government Printing Office, March 1963), p. 100.

the size of his paycheck, the length of his car, the noise he must endure, the people to whom he is permitted to talk—these are some of the clues to his relative place in the hierarchy of positions in the American society. High on the list is the length of time he has been required to sit in some schoolroom in order to gain entry to an eventual social niche. Not all of these status symbols are unworthy of notice, but there is surprisingly little attention paid to real learning and knowledge, and scant concern about whether or not a person actually contributes to the productive effort of the nation.

One of the most important symbols down through the years has been the bachelor degree. In some ways it carries a greater status value than an advanced degree. It certainly is vastly more significant than a lesser educational credential. Only those with an impeccable family position in a community, or those who have some rare, innate gift, can override its absence. Its attainment stamps the individual as one who has somehow entered the "circle," whether or not his exposure to the educational process has made him either more learned or more productive. It carries no stigma of intellectualism and, at the same time, erases the question mark of doubt about intelligence.

The graduate of the technical institute, unfortunately, lacks the bachelor degree. He also lacks the title of professional. His education has not been liberal. He has pursued a program of study designed specifically to prepare him to work. He occupies a position that is not only subordinate but also is designated as subordinate. Almost every position in life is subordinate to some other, but this fact is often ignored. A foreman is subordinate to a superintendent, a superintendent to a plant manager, and a plant manager to a president. Yet in each case the fact is not emphasized. In educational circles a department chairman is subordinate to a dean, and a dean, in turn, to a provost. But here again each level suppresses the negative aspects of the subordinate role and emphasizes the genuine worth of the effort. This is not so with the technician. He is trained to help an engineer or scientist and almost every utterance about his position underscores this fact.

Society seems to have conspired to keep retelling the technician what his position is, lest he forget. Moreover, he works with his hands. Like the dentist, the surgeon, or the pianist, his skill is combined with his knowledge to make him the talented performer he is.

But unlike the surgeon, whom society hails because of his technique, the technician receives the meager plaudits which are his because of his knowledge, and in his knowledge he is inevitably second best.

Finally, the technician is not a member of any "group." He is cut off from management and labor and is denied affiliation with professional technical societies in all but a few instances. Even when he is permitted identification with a technical society, it is in an associate or auxiliary role. Loosely knit and somewhat apologetic as a group, technicians have been unable to form any genuinely cohesive technical or social association of their own. Attempts have been made to organize from time to time, but such organizations have sputtered and failed. The technicians must look elsewhere for fraternity. Lacking organization, they lack a forum in which they can discuss common problems, and they lack a sounding board to give clarity and articulation to their wants, needs, and aspirations.

On the whole, society has treated technicians shabbily, and what recognition they have received has been grudging, dilatory, and misguided. Yet this society, which could not exist without technicians, treats them as secondary at every turn; this same society, however, has the effrontery to be amazed and even angry because technicians are in such short supply.

The attitude of industry.   A large segment of industry reflects and generates this attitude of society. If other factors are roughly equivalent, most industries will employ an engineer rather than a technician to fill a technician-level assignment. This practice is defended by the argument that the engineer has a higher theoretical ceiling. The long-range view that this practice depresses the technician supply is seldom taken, or even recognized. In this connection, the engineers themselves contribute to the misuse of manpower by accepting subprofessional employment. In so doing they place their own professional status in jeopardy, add their bit to the clouded question about whether the shortage of engineers is real or synthetic, and help postpone the time when more people will be drawn into the technician fold. No physician would volunteer for a nurse's post; in fact, he would perform a nurse's duties only in a crucial situation. In behaving thus, he rigorously protects his professional position and contributes unmistakably to the public image of the nurse as one who is critically needed, who serves in a definitive role, and who has a personal dignity all her own. The engineer apparently sees this total picture only dimly. He may complain, yet by his actions he cooperates with industry in a practice that stifles the development of *bona fide* technicians and hinders the national productive effort.

Much of industry contributes further to the retardation of technician development and displays its myopic view of the total situation by a careless and at times devious use of position titles. With an almost brash abandon, it assigns technicians such titles as "junior engineer," "junior scientist," "technical engineer," and a host of others. Responsible engineering bodies and engineering educators resent this bitterly. The Engineers' Council for Professional Development categorically denies accreditation to a technical institute curriculum which purports to graduate engineers regardless of the merit of the program. The National Society of Professional Engineers brings pressure to bear upon an individual practitioner who classifies himself as a professional engineer if he is not duly registered. But industry, as represented by some of the most powerful corporations in the world, ruthlessly exploits the status value of the title "engineer" to mollify technicians whose true position title gets them scant respect.

Thus, industry works against its own ultimate best interests and denies to technicians the solid build-up which, in the long run, would enhance their recognition by society. Unless big corporations alter their course, the technician and the technical institute will struggle in a bootstrap operation against impossible odds in the quest for adequate recognition.

The attitude of educators.   Like so many people in industry, the majority of educators have contributed their bit to the negative attitude of society toward the technical institute and the technician. College professors and administrators in higher education have tried diligently to keep themselves detached. Although they are not outspoken or critical most of the time, they carefully maintain a personal aloofness which insulates them from too close an identification with the technical institute. This kind of behavior is understandable, since it is in keeping with the long-standing, cherished, and completely false notion that identification with higher-level academic programs somehow makes the professor a better person. The confusion of ideas that has caused society to believe that the person in a so-called better job is therefore a better person is just as disturbingly present among college professors as among others. Obviously, if it is less desirable to teach in an undergraduate program than in a graduate one, it is still less desirable to teach in a technical institute program.

In fact, the mere presence of a "terminal" program on campus convinces many that the whole school must operate under questionable standards of excellence. This position is defended by many arguments, but the underlying reason is seldom clearly stated: that the presence of such programs may lower the prestige of the institution. It is even present among certain engineering educators. These educators believe that while the technical institute may have a place in the scheme of things, it should be moved discreetly to somewhere else. While there are exceptions to this general position of both schools and faculties, the number of exceptions is small compared to the total. The majority are quite uneasy about the presence of a technical institute and feel more comfortable in a school situation of which it is not a part.

The distinguished universities which have undertaken technical institute programs have made a distinct inroad on this over-all position. In time it may become an accepted practice to place such curriculums in institutions having well-established engineering schools, and thereby to create the rapport that will give understanding and sympathetic treatment to the education of technicians. Such integration seems a long time coming, however, when one considers the fact that in the face of a mounting need for technicians only a handful of universities have actually taken such action. The long-run decision may be to isolate technical institute curriculums in separate institutions completely detached from comprehensive universities. Only time will give this final answer. During the interim the technical institute will remain an educational activity of uncertain status. The behavior of college educators in the past suggests that there is little likelihood of change.

Accrediting bodies have done more to give recognition to technical institute education than the faculties or administrators of colleges have done, although one scarcely could argue that this recognition has been anything but cautious. The Middle States Association and the Engineers' Council for Professional Development have contributed without any question to the enhancement of technical institute education. Many other agencies have been slow to act and, in effect, have retarded the development of this important segment of education. On the whole, the net effect has tended more to circumscribe than to stimulate growth. To have well-defined categories of educational institutions, and to refuse even to examine those institutions which do not fit nicely into existing patterns, dampens enthusiasm for innovation and thwarts progressive development of educational programs geared to a swiftly changing industrial economy. It is to be hoped that this simply attests to the basic stability of social institutions and does not depict the reactionary attitude of a smug society.

Secondary school people also have done little to give impetus to the technical institute movement. Caught in the complex of student yearning, parental myopia, and university aloofness, the high school counselor threads a careful path through his maze. Most high school teachers, including counselors, are not very well informed about the technical institute. They tend to counsel the better students to go to four-year colleges, and they take some pride in and genuinely deserved credit for the successes of their graduates in college, particularly in difficult curriculums at distinguished universities. They view with some misgiving the private schools offering terminal, specialized programs—especially if such schools are proprietary operations. Moreover, few students know what they really want or where they will work upon graduation, so general education appears to be the better choice. In the end not many students are counseled to become technicians, and this fact in itself is a deterrent to the fruitful development of the technical institute.

For very human and understandable reasons, parents generally tend to detract from the status the technical institute deserves. They hesitate to send their children to a school which lacks the glamour so frequently associated with the word "college." Everyone is the product of his own experience, and most people are limited by it. In the peculiar pattern of American life, schooling is not a happy experience for most people. Adults who look back upon their carefree school days do not recall the classroom, but rather the appendages to the central school experience. Athletic events, fraternities or clubs, proms and parties, and the fellowship of schoolmates play a heavy role in memories. So also do the intellectual embellishments: the world-famous laboratory, the percentage of Ph.D.'s on the faculty, the Nobel prize winners, the distinguished author. Only a few of these attractive features contribute significantly to the academic learning of a student. Good teachers, good curriculums and good facilities are most directly responsible for accomplishing the stated purposes of a school, yet they get sidetracked as the years blur the memory of most adults.

A parent often is attracted by the glamour features of an educational institution and, if he can see no major obstacle barring the path, will guide his child to such a place. These features at times will mar his vision of his child's interests and capabilities so that his counsel is sometimes harmful. It is unfortunate that technical institutes so often lack many of these externals, while offering precisely the educational program which many students want and need. But parents, not wanting to place a ceiling (either educationally or socially) upon the growth of their children, tend to by-pass the technical institute. In so doing, they add their small part to the total weight against which the technical institute must push to gain recognition.

Some positive aspects. Not all attitudes and actions of society are negative to the technical institute. Since the late 1950's a number of federal government agencies have hammered hard on the technician theme. The Executive Office of the President, the Congress, the U.S. Office of Education, and the Civil Service have made clear the role the technician plays in the economy and the dependence of national productivity upon his work. A number of states also have investigated the possibility of enabling legislation which would take the burden of financing technical institutes off private institutions. Slowly, but inevitably, the impact of government action will be felt.

Some industries have made careful studies of their own operations to determine how they can make better use of technicians. A few have definite recruitment, training, and placement programs for technicians, just as for engineers, scientists, and others. Eventually, most industries will follow the lead of the few in order to remain competitive.

Professional educators have not been so fervent in their concern about the plight of the technician in society as many believe they should be, but there are many exceptions to this. Leland L. Medsker, James W. Thornton, Ralph R. Fields, and Edmund L. Gleazer, for example, have sensed the role that the junior-community college should take and have written forcefully on this point. Maurice W. Roney, while with the United States Office of Education, made prodigious contributions in the vocational-technical field. Henry Adams, Kenneth Holderman, and Lawrence Johnson, to name only three, have lucidly portrayed the part that complex university systems can play. These and other gifted and conscientious leaders in various segments of education have devoted much effort to raising the status of the technician and his education.

The actions of technical societies associated with engineering have been the most dramatic in contributing to the rise of technicians in the United States. As mentioned in previous chapters, the American Society for Engineering Education has taken genuine leadership in the movement to improve the status of technicians. This organization not only acts through its Technical Institute Division to focus attention upon the problems of technician education, but also has sponsored two areas of awards for individuals who make outstanding contributions. One of these is the James H. McGraw Award given annually to a person whose cumulative actions in the field have been truly significant. The other is the Arthur L. Williston Award which recognizes distinguished contributors to the literature in the technical institute field. The Engineers' Council for Professional Development, through its program for the accreditation of engineering-technology curriculums, has assumed a responsibility for technician education of unquestioned magnitude.

The National Society of Professional Engineers has directed its attention to the role of the technician as a member of the industrial society rather than to his education *per se*. As stated by A. C. Friel, N.S.P.E. is concerned about the utilization and employment conditions of engineering technicians as well as with their status and related problems.[19] To implement action to this end, the society established the Institute for the Certification of Engineering Technicians in 1961.

Operated by a board of trustees composed of both engineers and technicians, the institutes certifies technicians in three grades: junior engineering technician, engineering technician, and senior engineering technician. The structure, governing policy, and operational procedure of the institute were described by its first board chairman, Merritt A. Williamson, in an article published in *The American*

19 A. C. Friel, "Institute Recommended to Certify Technicians," *The American Engineer* (October 1960).

Engineer in September of 1962.[20] The institute is an examining body which exists wholly for the purpose of determining the competency of those who voluntarily apply for certification. It could be that this institute will enable technicians to achieve that cohesiveness and articulation so desperately needed in society's industrial and social complex. Whether or not it will remains to be seen. There is no question about the fact, however, that this action by N.S.P.E. is aimed directly at the core of the technician problem.

Summary

The individual in the technical institute is much like the student in any college program. Though somewhat older than the average, he has basically the same motivations and goals and the same concern for learning how to achieve his place in the complicated industrial society of this era. This society is crucially in need of technicians, who play a vital role in the economy. Almost every segment of industry can utilize well-qualified technicians, but there is an alarming lack of rapport between the employers who need their services and the schools which give them their preparation. Society in general is uninformed about the important role technicians play and the vital need for technical institutes. Some schools, industries, and technical groups, plus a few courageous and far-sighted individuals, however, are making conspicuous efforts to remedy this situation.

---

[20] Merritt A. Williamson, "The Institute for the Certification of Engineering Technicians," *The American Engineer* (September 1962).

Bibliography

Annual Reports. New York: The Engineers' Council for Professional Development.

Bethel, Lawrence L., Jesse P. Bogue, and Frank B. Lindsay, *Junior College Technical Education in Your Community.* New York: McGraw-Hill Book Co., 1948.

Bogue, Jesse P., *The Community College.* New York: McGraw-Hill Book Co., 1950.

Henninger, Ross G., *The Technical Institute in America.* New York: Mc-Graw-Hill Book Co., 1959.

Kovol, Alexander G., *Soviet Education For Science And Technology.* New York: John Wiley & Sons, Inc., 1957.

McGraw, James L., *Characteristics of Excellence in Engineering Technology Education.* Urbana, Illinois: American Society For Engineering Education, 1962.

Payne, George L., *Britain's Scientific And Technological Manpower.* Stanford, California: Stanford University Press, 1960.

Smith, Leo F., and Laurence Lipsett, *The Technical Institute.* New York: McGraw-Hill Book Co., 1956.

Vocational Education Of College Grade, Bulletin No. 18. Washington, D.C.: U.S. Office of Education, 1946.

Vocational-Technical Training For Industrial Occupations, Bulletin No. 228. Washington, D.C.: U.S. Office of Education, Vocational Division, 1944.

Wickenden, William E. and Robert H. Spahr, *A Study Of Technical Institutes.* Lancaster, Pa.: Society for the Promotion of Engineering Education, 1931.

PERIODICALS

The American Engineer, New York, N.Y.

Junior College Journal, Washington, D.C.

Journal Of Engineering Education, Lancaster, Pa.

Technical Education News, New York, N.Y.

Index

A

Academic rank, 83
Accreditation, 68
Adams, Henry, 110
Administration, 17, 18, 30–49
Africa, 17
American Association of Collegiate Schools of Business, 71
American Association of Junior Colleges, 19, 21
American Chemical Society, 72
American Medical Association, 71
American Society for Engineering Education:
  awards, 110
  curriculum study, 68
  exchange mission to Soviet Union, 19, 20
  general education survey, 58, 60
  McGraw Report, 62
  manpower studies, 93
  meetings, 12
  teacher training, 86
  technical institute division, 72
  technical institute study, 10
  technician's work, 95
American Technical Education Association, 52
Arnold, W. M., 65, 66
Association of Professional Engineers of the Province of Ontario, 19
Atomic Energy Commission, 86
Australia, 17

B

Beatty, H. Russell, 52, 60
Bethel, Lawrence L., 40
Bogue, Jesse P., 13, 40
Booher, Edward E., 60, 61
Brademus, John, 23
Bradley University, 9, 35
Britain's Scientific and Technical Manpower, 18
Brooklyn Polytechnic Institute, 9
Broome Technical Community College, 41
Bucher, E. E., 47
Bureau of Labor Statistics, 24, 100

C

California, 12, 41, 42
Canada, 17, 18
Carnegie Institute of Technology, 9, 35
Carson, R. G., 84
Central Technical Institute, 59
Certification, 110
Characteristics of "technical institutes," 4
Characteristics of Excellence in Engineering Technology Education, 53, 63, 64, 80
College grade or level, 4
Collins Radio Company, 101
Community college:
  accreditation, 71
  California, 41, 42
  educational philosophy, 13, 70
  influence, 14, 16
  organization and administration, 40
  technical colleges of New York, 40
  terminal curriculums, 43, 44
Complex university systems, 34
Cornell University, 85
Correspondence schools, 73
Cummings, Kimbal C., 98
Curriculum:
  characteristics, 4
  criteria, 51
  length, 51
  model, 63, 66, 67
  rigor, 61
Curry, Herbert H., 86

D

Dauwalder, Donald D., 42
Dayton, University of, 35, 36
Definition of "Technical Institute," 1, 50
Denominational schools, 73
Departmental faculties, 81
Detroit, University of, 96
Dictionary of Education, 4, 50
District of Columbia, 26, 44
Dobrovolny, J. S., 86
Dow Chemical Company, 53
Draker, C. J., 101
Drexel Institute, 9, 35

115